THE TIDES

W9-BWQ-966

Edward P. Clancy, Professor of Physics and Chairman of the Physics Department at Mount Holyoke College in South Hadley, Massachusetts, has written on a topic which has fascinated him from boyhood. Though a midwesterner by upbringing, he was able to spend his summers on the coast of Maine where his grandfather, of a seafaring family, showed him the lore of the ocean and of sailing.

Dr. Clancy was born in Beloit, Wisconsin, and graduated from Beloit College. He then went to Harvard University on an Austin Fellowship to do graduate work in physics. He received his Ph.D. just before World War II, and joined the scientific staff of the newly organized Harvard Underwater Sound Laboratory. This laboratory was assigned responsibility for research in various aspects of underwater warfare—in particular, matters having to do with the propagation of sound waves beneath the ocean's surface.

"My trip from Wisconsin to Harvard was essentially a one-way affair," writes Dr. Clancy. "Figuratively speaking, I never again escaped from Massachusetts. But this is not a matter of regret. My family and I are close to the sea, and to our 18-foot centerboard sloop and our 27-foot Saint Pierre dory. The latter is a boat for all weather, and I sometimes take her out of the harbor during storms to see how much she (and I) can take of what the sea chooses to dish up."

Dr. Clancy is the author of various scientific papers, chiefly in the fields of physical optics and of the teaching of physics. In addition to his appointments at Harvard and at Mount Holyoke, he has been a Research Associate at the California Institute of Technology on a fellowship of the Fund for the Advancement of Education, and more recently a Research Associate at Harvard. He is a Past Chairman of the New England Section of the American Physical Society.

THE TIDES

PULSE OF THE EARTH

Edward P. Clancy

Illustrated by
Warren H. Maxfield

SCIENCE
STUDY
SERIES

Published by Anchor Books
Doubleday & Company, Inc.
Garden City, New York

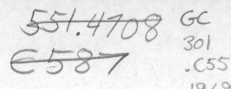

TO ELIZABETH

THE TIDES was originally published in a hardcover
edition by Doubleday & Company, Inc., in 1968

Anchor Books edition: 1969

THE SCIENCE STUDY SERIES

The Science Study Series offers to students and to the general public the writing of distinguished authors on the most stirring and fundamental topics of science, from the smallest known particles to the whole universe. Some of the books tell of the role of science in the world of man, his technology and civilization. Others are biographical in nature, telling the fascinating stories of the great discoverers and their discoveries. All the authors have been selected both for expertness in the fields they discuss and for ability to communicate their special knowledge and their own views in an interesting way. The primary purpose of these books is to provide a survey within the grasp of the young student or the layman. Many of the books, it is hoped, will encourage the reader to make his own investigations of natural phenomena.

The Series, which now offers topics in all the sciences and their applications, had its beginning in a project to revise the secondary schools' physics curriculum. At the Massachusetts Institute of Technology during 1956 a group of physicists, high school teachers, journalists, apparatus designers, film producers, and other specialists organized the Physical Science Study Committee, now operating as part of Education Development Center, Newton, Massachusetts. They pooled their knowledge and experience toward the design and creation of aids to the learning of physics. Initially their effort was supported by the National Science Foundation, which has continued to aid the program. The Ford Foundation, the Fund for the Advancement of Education, and the Alfred P. Sloan Foundation have also given support. The Committee has created a textbook, an extensive film series, a laboratory guide, especially designed apparatus, and a teachers' source book.

CONTENTS

PROLOGUE

To stand on a cliff at oceanside, the rock trembling under the surge and thrust of the great breakers, is to feel a pulse of the sea. Waves, born of the wind in its long reach, pound out on the shore their ceaseless rhythm.

But there is also a slower pulse to the sea—a pulse felt twice a day, felt more in the nooks and crannies and rivulets of the coast than on the bolder scarps. This is the pulse of the tide—slow, predictable, majestic in its sweep. Here, in a little arm of the Chesapeake, the tide's progress is measured in inches, and tiny sea creatures wriggle their leisurely way along its edge. Here, near the head of the Bay of Fundy, the sea comes racing over the sands, swirling in eddies, overwhelming the shallows, climbing the fish nets. Against these nets —hours earlier—men had stood, their ladders planted on dry ground, and plucked their harvest from the meshes. And farther on, funneled by narrowing shores and dragged by friction on a swiftly shoaling channel, the waters overreach themselves, tumbling and coursing in a "bore" up the Petitcodiac River.

This is the tide, gentle or violent, but always at the call of the moon and the sun. Few natural phenomena have as many and as regular commands over the ways of those who dwell by the sea or who bring their ships to its shores. And to the scientist the tides have their own fascination. He sees at work the tide-producing forces of gravitation—forces essentially simple, but leading to tidal phenomena which are not simple and which are indeed of the greatest variety.

It is well to say what this book is and what it is not. I have tried to tell, in small compass and with a minimum of technical language, what makes the tides, how we see them here and there in the world, how they complicate the life of the sailor, how men are harnessing them to generate power, and how they affect the future of the earth and of the moon.

In no sense is this a comprehensive study of the tides. For those who wish to know more, I have provided a list of suggested additional reading. Few books containing discussion of the tides have been published; to their authors, and to the authors of various articles on the subject in scientific journals, I am deeply indebted.

Chapter I

INTRODUCTION

Pliny on the tides

Pliny, a Roman born in A.D. 23 and killed in the volcanic eruption which destroyed Pompeii, was the author of many volumes on diverse subjects. Only his *Historia Naturalis* has survived to our time, however. In it he writes, "Much has been said about the nature of waters; but the most wonderful circumstance is the alternate flowing and ebbing of the tides, which exist, indeed, under various forms, but is caused by the sun and the moon. The tide flows twice and ebbs twice between each two risings of the moon, always in the space of twenty-four hours. First, the moon rising with the stars swells out the tide, and after some time, having gained the summit of the heavens, she declines from the meridian and sets, and the tide subsides. Again, after she has set, and moves the heavens under the earth, as she approaches the meridian on the opposite side, the tide flows in; after which it recedes until she again rises to us. But the tide of the next day is never at the same time with that of the preceding."

Pliny was an acute observer of natural phenomena. In his book he goes on to describe variations in tidal height as the month progresses, and speaks of curious local tidal behavior. Unfortunately, for all his critical faculties Pliny was most uncritical in his acceptance of folklore. He records in his volume, from hearsay, all sorts of obviously incredible statements.

Tidal phenomena, then, were known to the ancients. But since their civilization centered for the most part around the Mediterranean, where tides scarcely exist, it was those travelers venturing into the Atlantic who returned with wondrous stories of the rise and fall of the sea. To most inhabitants of the early Mediterranean civilizations, however, unused to separating fact from fable, tales of large-scale tidal phenomena were met with some skepticism.

Caesar's "invasion" of Kent

Certainly Caesar, as he planned his first invasion of Britain, was largely unaware of what he was to encounter on the Kentish coast. His was the first assault landing in force whose details are well recorded. He faced, as did many commanders of assault landings on Pacific isles during World War II, a shore whose nature he knew little about. That there were outlying shoals he was aware, and he was presumably somewhat familiar with tides as they behaved on the French coast. The point of assemblage for his invasion was the harbor of what is now Boulogne.

The site chosen for landing in Britain was a stretch of beach near Dover, at a point where no cliffs obstructed a movement inland. The large transports and the galleys, carrying foot soldiers, were allowed to ground out near the shore and after severe fighting with the local defenders a beachhead was secured. Then the galleys were drawn up on the beach, and the transports were anchored offshore. The eighteen cavalry vessels which started later were greatly needed. They had met a gale, however; most were blown back to the French coast where they found refuge.

On the shore of East Kent the wind was still raging,

though a full moon shone through the scattered clouds. Hard as it is to believe, it would appear that Caesar and his officers were ignorant of the connection between moon and tide. High water came about an hour before midnight—even higher than usual for a near-spring tide because of seas driven by the gale. The beached galleys, supposedly above high water mark, were swept by the breakers; the anchored transports were driven ashore. Some vessels were totally wrecked, and all sustained heavy damage. Stores were lost; repairs could not be made to the ships because tools had been left in the embarkation port. Finally a galley was sent back to France for equipment, and using materials from twelve ships wrecked beyond repair, the others were made sufficiently ready for the return voyage. October was approaching, with its inevitable stormy weather, and Caesar, not daring to postpone his departure by following up his initial victory, returned to France.

Without reading Caesar's own version of the affair it would be difficult to see why, when his dispatches reached the Roman Senate, a thanksgiving period of twenty days was ordained in honor of his exploits!

Tidal regularities

If Caesar had made careful observations of tidal phenomena over a reasonably long period of time—an operation for which he was obviously temperamentally not fitted—he would have discovered certain simple regularities. He would have seen that the sea rises and falls nearly twice a day—nearly, because the interval from one high tide to the next is not twelve hours, but about twelve hours and twenty-five minutes. Every day, then, high water comes later by about fifty minutes. To relate this fact to the moon is easy, since the moon reaches its highest point overhead (as the astronomer would say, it crosses the *meridian*) about fifty minutes later on each succeeding day. This is not to imply that the two events occur at the same time; high water comes in general some hours after or before the passage of the moon, and furthermore this time differential depends on the time of the month.

Another aspect of the tides is their height. Even Caesar must have noticed how one tide may vary from another. At certain places, for example, the night tide reaches higher than that of the day. Furthermore, a ledge seen to be still well covered at low water may be laid entirely bare a fortnight later. This fortnightly variation correlates almost exactly with successive appearances of the new and of the full moon. Soon after these events, we find that the tide has its greatest range from low to high water; when the moon is in its first or its third quarter the range is a minimum. The largest variations are called *spring* tides, and the smallest are called *neaps*. The term *spring* has nothing to do with the season of the year; it derives from "springing," or lively, water. *Neap* comes from the Anglo-Saxon *nep* —scant, or lacking.

Local variations in tides

So far we have been speaking of tides as they appear in general. But one of the fascinations of studying the tides is the variety of their behavior. Local conditions— the configuration of the land, the shape of the sea bottom—may cause the rise and fall of the water to follow an unusual course. In some places, there is only one tide a day. In others, there is little if any tide in the sense of rise and fall, but tremendous currents sweep back and forth on a regular schedule, currents which are as much a tidal phenomenon as changing height of water.

Seiches, forced oscillations

It is ordinarily in closed, or semi-closed, basins that the more unusual behavior is noticed. Tides, of a sort, may even be found in lakes. They seldom amount to more than a few inches, and are called *seiches*. The word apparently derives from the Latin *siccus*, or dry, but the connection in meaning, if any, is a mystery the philologists have not solved.

Unless a lake is large, its seiches are more usually set up by strong winds or by changes in atmospheric pressure than by the gravitational effects which account for the ocean tides. If the water has been pushed away from its level position, it tends to return when the disturbing force is removed. The inertia involved is large, however, and the moving mass of water "overshoots," somewhat in the manner of a swinging pendulum. Thus an oscillation is set up, occurring at a rate which depends on the size and contour of the lake's shore and the depth of its bottom.

When the body of water is not a lake but a bay open to the ocean, large tides may be found. If the mouth of the bay were closed, the water in it, like that of the lake, would have a natural period of oscillation. But in actuality the bay communicates with the sea, whose tidal rise and fall feeds energy into the waters of the bay and sets them swinging in time with the ocean tide. The term used by physicists in this connection is "forced oscillation." If you have studied physics, you know that when an outside force is applied to a system at just the same rate as the system would vibrate if left to itself, then a phenomenon called *resonance* occurs. If frictional effects are not too great, the "vibrations" may become very large in a resonant situation. In terms of the old fables, a wine glass shatters when the soprano hits the right note, or a bridge collapses when soldiers march across it with their steps in just the right (or wrong!) cadence. In a bay or estuary, the phenomenon creates violent tidal currents through the mouth and large ranges of tides within, if the ocean's rise and fall coincides with the natural resonant frequency for "swinging" of the water within the basin. If, on the other hand, there is little correlation between the two periods, there may still be large currents at the mouth of the harbor. They are to be thought of as simply filling and emptying a vessel, however, and the total rise and fall of water is ordinarily not impressive.

Bores

An effect, often quite spectacular, occurs when with an incoming tide the water is funneled into an ever-narrowing channel. This can be the case when a river, whose last portion consists of tidal water, ends at the sea. The inrushing water must accelerate, and typically at the same time encounters a shallowing channel. Frictional effects on that part of the water near the bottom slow it down; the water above tends to retain its momentum, however. The situation is analogous to that of a long swell approaching a beach; the friction of the bottom causes the wave to form an ever-steeper front until finally the top falls over and forward. For the tidal water advancing up the river, however, the effect is continuous. Unlike the case of the wave on the beach, the water behind is constantly rising. Thus the steepening wave front soon collapses upon itself in a welter of foam and continues to rush on up the river. This is called a *bore,* and we will talk about it in more detail in a later chapter.

Effect of wind and of changing barometric pressure

We have spoken of regularities—daily, semi-daily, fortnightly—in the tides. But we have also mentioned the possible complicating effects of winds and changes in barometric pressure. The careful observer of tides finds that superimposed on the regularities traceable to the sun and moon are other day-to-day, largely unpredictable, effects. Most of these can be laid to the weather.

Wind, blowing across even an initially smooth water surface, encounters friction. In technical language, a "shearing stress" is set up, and some of the momentum of the wind is communicated to the water. Waves are soon formed, and the frictional effect increases because the rough surface induces turbulent effects in the air. To analyze the matter in detail is a most complicated problem in aerodynamics, still largely unsolved. The result is obvious, however. There is a tendency for the water to be pushed along by the wind, and in violent storms the effects may be dramatic. They are particularly impressive when the storm's surge coincides with the natural time of high water. Breakwaters, built to withstand the punishment of waves crashing against them at normal levels, disintegrate when they are overtopped by huge seas, and thus eroded from behind. Wind surges are, of course, very apt to occur with hurricanes. Ordinarily, more damage is done by the combination of high water and huge seas than by the direct effect of wind.

Tidal disturbances due to changes in atmospheric pressure are demonstrable; the explanation is more subtle, however, than in the case of the wind. Furthermore, the two effects are usually superimposed, and therefore hard to separate since storms are accompanied by lively behavior of the barometer. In any case, one can make certain rough calculations as to the magnitude of the effect. Mercury has a specific gravity of 13.6. A change of one inch in atmospheric pressure, as measured by a mercury barometer, thus corresponds to a variation in sea level of about thirteen inches. Where the pressure is high, the sea is depressed.

The result can be much magnified, however, if the storm system is a fast-moving one and a region of low pressure is traveling at a speed close to that of the normal "tidal wave" in the particular area. (We shall shortly be considering the origin and nature of these waves.) In that case a resonance can occur in which the atmospheric trough produces a strong elevation in sea level.

Chapter II

ISAAC NEWTON AND THE
EQUILIBRIUM THEORY OF THE TIDES

Tides and the Principia

It was to Isaac Newton, that intellectual giant of science, that men owed their first real understanding of why the tides behave as they do. Newton's *Philosophiae Naturalis Principia Mathematica* (usually referred to as the *Principia*) appeared in first edition in 1686. In his preface—dated May 8 of that year—Newton says, ". . . in the third [Book] I derive from the celestial phenomena the forces of gravity with which bodies tend to the sun and several planets. Then from these forces, by other propositions which are also mathematical, I deduce the motions of the planets, the comets, the moon, and the sea."

In reading those parts of the *Principia* which deal with the tides, one senses Newton's exultation in the ability of his theory to explain the rise and fall of the sea. It is, in fact, not generally recognized how large a part this success played in Newton's final satisfaction with his own theory.

Newton actually accounted for the more general aspects of tidal phenomena in great detail. With his law of gravitation he calculated the height of the midocean lunar and solar tides, and explained the variations in tidal height with the time of month, time of year, and with latitude. His investigations, however, were largely limited to what is now called the equilibrium theory of the tides. But the tide is essentially a dynamic phenomenon. Masses of water move, and—as Newton himself would surely have admitted—his equilibrium theory must be extended to account for all that is observed. Newton did, indeed, try to introduce some dynamical arguments to explain certain tidal phenomena which differed from those predicted by the equilibrium theory. Later, in his *Mécanique Céleste*, Laplace showed these arguments to be largely incorrect.

Nevertheless, the following brief description of the equilibrium theory will serve as an introduction to our understanding of why the tides behave as they do. Later, we shall see how dynamical effects modify the action of the tides.

Law of gravitation

The gravitational attraction of the earth and moon result in so-called *tide-generating forces*. To describe these forces fully would require a good deal of mathematical detail—probably more than you would want to work through. But if you recall Newton's law of gravitation, it is easy to see in a semi-quantitative way what is involved. The law states that every element of mass in the universe attracts every other element with a force proportional to their masses and inversely proportional to the square of the distance r between them. If their masses are respectively m_1 and m_2, and if f is the magnitude of the force, then we may write

$$f = \frac{G m_1 m_2}{r^2}.$$

Here, G is the universal gravitational constant. Its value is

$$6.67 \times 10^{-11} \frac{\text{newton-(meter)}^2}{\text{(kilogram)}^2}.$$

To apply this fundamental concept to the attraction between two large-scale objects, we must realize that the force we observe is actually the vector sum of a great many pairs of forces. Each of the elements of mass which together make up the first object attracts each of the other elements of the second object, and vice versa. As a result, the total force of attraction between the two objects is what mathematicians would call a double summation, taken over all the possible pairs of attracting elements.

Obviously, the distance between a given pair of elements varies with their location within their respective objects. If the objects are irregular in shape there is no easy way of calculating the force between them.

For *spherical* objects, however, the situation is different (and fortunately most celestial bodies are approximately spherical). Newton was able to prove—and in the process he had to invent the calculus—that the attraction between two spheres is the same as if all of their mass is concentrated at their centers. The force between earth and moon, then, can be written to a high degree of accuracy as

$$F = G \frac{m_M m_E}{R^2}$$

where m_M and m_E are respectively the total mass of the moon and the earth, and R is the distance between their centers. A similar relation exists for the force between sun and earth.

To simplify matters, let us "abolish" the sun for the moment and consider the tidal forces produced on the earth by the moon alone. The earth-moon system is pictured in Figure 1, which is obviously not drawn to scale—the moon as shown is much too close to the earth. Earth and moon revolve about a common center of gravity CG, which—interestingly enough—is within the earth because of the earth's much greater mass relative to that of the moon.

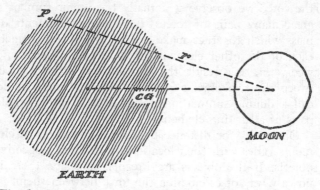

Fig. 1   Earth-moon system.

Between the moon and any object on or in the earth, there exists a force of attraction. If a mass m is at the point P, say, then the attraction between m and the moon is

$$F = G\,\frac{m_M m}{r^2}.$$

If we chop the earth up into a great many fragments of mass m and write an expression like the above for each fragment, then the totality of all these forces F will be the gravitational force between the earth and the moon. Notice, however, that those parts of the earth for which r is smaller will be subject to a greater pull from the moon than those for which r is larger. In this simple fact lies, as we shall see, the origin of the tide-generating forces.

Centripetal and centrifugal force

If the force between earth and moon is one of attraction, why do they not move closer together? The answer lies in the fact that each of these two celestial objects is "orbiting" the other—i.e., each moves in a circle around a common center of gravity. To make an object move in a circle, a centripetal force must be supplied. Figure 2 shows the location and direction of such a force. Here a stone is being whirled around in a horizontal circle on the end of a string. Because any

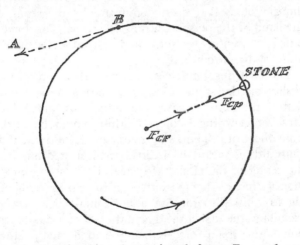

Fig. 2 Relationship of centripetal force F_{CP} and centrifugal force F_{CF} for a stone whirling around on the end of a string.

object not moving in a straight line is accelerating (Newton's first law of motion), and because an unbalanced, net force must be applied in the direction of an acceleration to produce that acceleration (Newton's second law), then in the case of motion in a circle an acceleration exists in the direction of the center of the circle and a *centripetal force* must be applied to produce it. In the situation of Figure 2, the centripetal force F_{CP} is produced by the inward pull of the string on the stone.

Newton's third law says that for every force there exists somewhere in the system an equal and opposite force. Contrary to what is a common misunderstanding, this opposing force is never applied to *the same object* as the first force. If it were, the effects of the two forces would always cancel, and nowhere in the universe could there be an acceleration! In the example we have been discussing, the opposing force can be thought of as that exerted outward by the string on the hand of the person whirling the stone. This force is called the *centrifugal force* and is represented in Figure 2 by the arrow F_{CF}.

The centrifugal force is *not*, we see, a force which pushes on the stone. One often hears the statement that if the string breaks, the stone flies outward because of centrifugal force. Nothing could be farther from the truth. The stone does not fly outward if by "outward" is meant in a direction measured out from the center of the circle. Moreover, if the string breaks, then *no* force is being exerted on the stone (by choosing to whirl the stone in a horizontal circle, we are excluding the effect of gravitation from our discussion). And if no force is being exerted on the stone, it will continue to move in a straight line in a direction which is its motion at the instant the string broke —i.e., in a direction tangent to the circle. The arrow *AB*, then, would be the direction of the stone if the string broke when the stone was at point *B*.

How tide-generating forces arise

Forget, for the moment, the rotation of the earth on its own axis. This rotation plays no part in our present discussion, and it will simplify matters if we assume that it is zero. We have, then, only the earth-moon system revolving around its common center of gravity as shown in Figure 3. But if this is happening, and the earth is at the same time not rotating about its

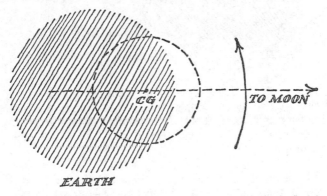

Fig. 3 Path of earth's center as it moves (dashed circle) around the common center of gravity *CG* of the earth-moon system.

own axis, a moment's thought will show that each particle of the earth is simply moving in a circle of exactly the same size as that of the dashed circle in Figure 3. The dashed circle represents the path in space of the earth's center as it revolves about the earth-moon's center of gravity *CG*. You can visualize this motion more easily, perhaps, if you place a coin on a table top, put your finger on the coin, and move the coin in a circle. The coin, obviously, is not rotating about its own center, but nevertheless it is moving in a circle.

For example, consider Figure 4. Here P_1 and P_2 are respectively the points on the earth farthest from and nearest to the moon. As the center of the earth moves around the dashed circle (as in Figure 3), the point

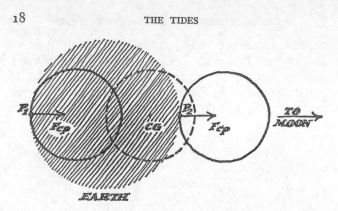

Fig. 4 Paths traced out by the points P_1 and P_2 (solid circles), and by the earth's center (dashed circle), as earth and moon revolve about their common center of gravity *CG*. The necessary centripetal force F_{CP} on an object placed at P_1 or P_2 is shown.

P_1 moves around the solid circle at the left and P_2 around the solid circle at the right. An object at P_1 or P_2 must therefore be subject to a centripetal force toward the center of its own circle. These forces F_{CP} are drawn. Note that for both P_1 and P_2 the directions of the forces are the same (and if the masses at P_1 and P_2 are equal, the magnitudes of the forces will also be the same).

Now look at Figure 5. Each of the points P_3 and P_4 is going around in its own circle as shown—circles quite displaced from those of P_1 and P_2, but nevertheless equal in size. Masses placed at P_3 and P_4 are thus subject to exactly the same centripetal forces as those at P_1 and P_2; note especially that these forces are parallel to those operating in Figure 4, and therefore parallel to the line joining the earth and moon.

A general conclusion may then be drawn: no matter where on the earth an object is located, the centripetal force on it necessary to make it travel in its own particular "orbit" is equal in magnitude and direction to

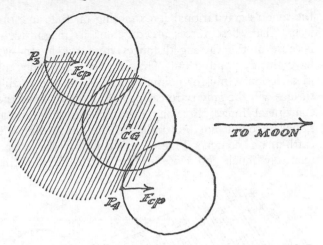

Fig. 5 Paths described by objects at points P_3 and P_4.

the centripetal force on any other object of the same mass. The situation is summarized in Figure 6 where the solid arrows pointing to the right represent the centripetal forces we have been discussing.

It is now time to relate these centripetal forces to

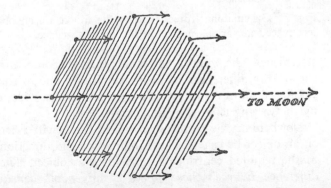

Fig. 6 Centripetal forces, due to rotation of the earth-moon system about its common center of gravity, on an object placed at various points on the earth's surface.

the moon's gravitational forces acting on the same objects. That these forces are different in magnitude—because of the varying distances from the moon—we have already pointed out. The forces are also different in direction. Only for points P_1 and P_2 on the earth's surface will the gravity forces be in the direction of the centripetal forces. For any other place, the gravitational force will not be parallel to the line joining the earth-moon centers. Figure 7, depicting the moon relatively much too close to the earth, clarifies this

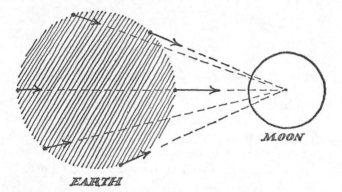

EARTH

Fig. 7 Gravitational forces, due to the moon, on an object placed at various points on the earth's surface.

statement. The gravity forces at various points are shown; the differences in their magnitudes due to the varying distances from the moon are made evident by the varying lengths of the arrows.

Nowhere on the earth's surface will the gravity force on an object be exactly equal in amount and direction to the required centripetal force for that object. *The difference between these forces at any point constitutes the tide-generating force at that point, and the totality of these differences over the whole earth is the basis of all tidal action.*

Figure 8 helps us to understand the matter. Here the arrows marked F_G represent the gravity forces, and the arrows marked F_{CP} the necessary centripetal forces. Tide-generating forces are shown by short arrows. Sup-

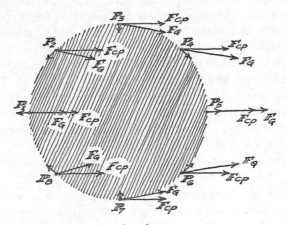

Fig. 8 The tide-generating forces.

pose the whole earth to be covered with ocean; there is no dry land. At regions in the vicinity of P_5, the gravitational force is greater than the necessary centripetal force, and the excess (short arrow) causes a bulging of the ocean's surface in the direction of the moon. Near P_1, the force of gravity is less than the necessary centripetal force, and the result is *in effect* a force in a direction away from the moon, producing a second bulge of water diametrically opposite the first one. A physicist, speaking more precisely but inevitably more technically, would say that the ocean's surface assumes an "equilibrium configuration" or *equipotential surface* which corresponds to an effective gravity field. This effective field consists of the "regular" gravity field plus the modification of that field by the dynamical effects of rotation we have been discussing.

At points P_3 and P_7, the tide-generating force is radially inward; it has no component along the surface. At points P_2, P_4, P_6, and P_8, however, we see that the force is chiefly parallel to the earth's surface, i.e., horizontal. By horizontal component, then, is meant that force which to an observer is directed along the level.

Only the horizontal component is of consequence in creating the tides. This component produces the horizontal displacement of water which is called the tidal wave, and from the tidal wave follow all tidal phenomena. Why may we dismiss the radial forces as unimportant? The answer is as follows: Compared to the ordinary gravitational force of the earth on an object on the earth's surface—i.e., compared to the object's weight—the tidal forces are extremely small. For the sake of clarity, the magnitude of the tidal forces has been greatly exaggerated in our diagram; we have always drawn the figures as if the moon were very close to the earth. If one actually calculates the amount of these forces (unfortunately, this calculation would carry us into more mathematical operations than we had better try to do here), it turns out that even their maximum value is only about one nine-millionth of the earth's gravitational force. All that the radial component of the tide-generating force can do is to change—*very* slightly—the magnitude of the earth's gravitation. As someone has said, "When the moon is over a small ship the vessel is lighter by the equivalent of the skipper's hat!"

If the radial components of the tidal force are so small, are not the horizontal components equally small? Yes. Here, however, the effect is different. Even a tiny horizontal force can give appreciable motion to a body of water. Again assuming an earth entirely covered with ocean, we see that the water will move until "bulges" are formed in the region where the moon is directly overhead and also in the region on the opposite side of the earth. Figure 9, in which the arrows represent the horizontal tide-generating forces, helps us to see why the bulges are created.

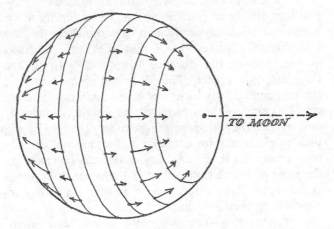

Fig. 9 The arrows represent the horizontal tide-generating forces.

What determines how high the bulges get? As soon as a bulge is formed there is a tendency for the water to flow back downhill. Thus a bulge will rise only to the extent that the tide-generating force is exactly balanced by the desire of the water to move away from the elevated region. From then on—in the equilibrium theory of the tides, at least—the situation will be static; the ocean covering the earth has assumed an egg-like shape, with the long axis of the egg pointing toward the moon.

Sun versus moon

So far we have been thinking of the tide as due to the moon alone. What part does the sun play? All that we have said about the effects of the moon's gravity acting on the ocean applies equally well to the sun. The sun is, of course, much farther away, but it is also much more massive.

The sun is, in fact, about 27 million times more massive than the moon, and about 390 times farther away. Mathematical analysis (which we omitted) of the tide-generating forces shows that they vary inversely as the *cube* of the distance from the earth to the tide-generating object. This does not deny Newton's law of gravitation, which says that gravitational forces vary inversely as the square of the distance. It simply means that the tide-generating forces, though having their origin in the force of gravitation, are not directly proportional to it. If tidal forces depend inversely on the cube of the distance, then if the moon were twice as far away, these forces would amount to only one-eighth their present value.

It is interesting—and important to our later discussions—to calculate the effect of the sun on the tides. Because of the sun's greater mass, its effect should be 27 million times larger than that of the moon. Because of its greater distance, its effect should be less by the amount $(1/390)^3$, or about 59 million times weaker. Thus the sun's tide-generating force is roughly 27/59 that of the moon, or a little less than half.

Direct measurement of tidal forces

The reader may be wondering at this point if there is any way of directly observing and measuring the tide-generating forces, rather than having to deduce them from theory or observe them indirectly from the way the tides behave. One might suppose, for example, that the horizontal component of the tide-generating force at a certain point on the earth's surface would cause a deflection from the vertical of a pendulum hung at that point. Indeed it does—but remember that the maximum value of the tidal forces is only about one nine-millionth of the earth's gravitational force. The corresponding angular motion is roughly two hundredths of a second of arc. So small an angle is hard to visualize. Sidewise displacement of the pendulum is easier to think about. To get a displacement of one inch, you would have to hang up a pendulum 160 miles long!

Does this mean that direct observation of the tide-generating forces is impossible? No, it can be done. A challenge such as this is often faced by the experimental scientist. He sees that a simple instrument—in this case an ordinary pendulum—is impractical for his purposes. He must devise apparatus of much greater sensitivity and therefore greater subtlety, apparatus with a supreme delicacy of response to a sidewise pull.

One solution is the "horizontal pendulum" shown in Figure 10a. A mass M is attached to the end of a

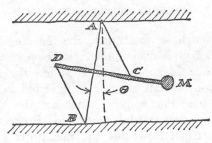

Fig. 10(a) Horizontal pendulum (side view).

rod perhaps 8 inches long. The rod is fastened to the center of an almost-vertical fiber AB, and held at right angles to that fiber by other restraining fibers, AC and BD. The fibers are typically of fused quartz, a material with excellent elastic properties and small sensitivity to changes in temperature.

The dashed line represents the vertical. Since AB is not quite vertical, the apparatus will tend to come to rest in the position shown. But suppose we make the angle θ very tiny indeed—say one second. Then, as you can readily see, even an extremely small sidewise force on M will make the rod turn (the force we are speaking of would be either into or out of the plane of the paper in the diagram).

In practice, the turning of the rod is measured after optical amplification of its motion. A small mirror is placed on the rod (Figure 10b). If a beam of light

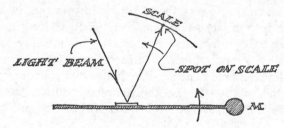

Fig. 10(b)   Horizontal pendulum (top view).

is made to fall on the mirror, the reflected beam can form a spot on a distant meter stick—perhaps on the opposite side of a large room. When the rod turns through some small angle, the reflected beam turns through twice that angle (remember the law of reflection—the angles of incidence and of reflection must always be equal). Because the measuring scale is so far away, the spot of light on it will have moved an appreciable distance even if the turning of the rod was scarcely visible.

Displacement of M from its rest position creates a twist in the fiber AB. The rod turns until the torque due to this twist (plus the tendency of M to "move back downhill") exactly counterbalances the torque due to the horizontal component of the tide-generating force. The travel of the light spot is thus a measure of the intensity of that force. Since only forces at right angles to the pendulum rod cause it to rotate, two of these pendulums placed crosswise to each other are necessary to measure the north-south and east-west components of the tide-generating force.

Apparatus of this sort shows beyond any doubt the existence and apparent magnitude of the horizontal component of the tide-generating force. There is a big complication, however. What did we mean, a moment ago, when we spoke of "the vertical"? Suppose that the earth is not rigid and itself yields somewhat to the tide-generating forces. How may we define *vertical* in that case? As we shall see in a later chapter, the earth is of course not rigid (nothing is), and to try to predict the magnitude of the ocean tides on the basis of the behavior of the horizontal pendulum is difficult.

There is another, and very interesting, experimental approach to the problem of measuring the horizontal component of the tide-generating forces. Suppose you took a length of garden hose (preferably transparent), filled it with water, and bent the ends up as shown in Figure 11. If horizontal forces are acting in the direction of the hose, a corresponding change in the levels of the water at the two ends should occur.

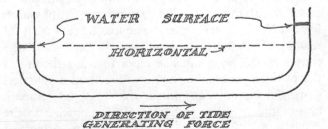

Fig. 11 Detection of horizontal component by means of water-filled tube.

The difference in level would be very small. Michelson did this experiment, using a glass tube 500 feet long. To observe the up-and-down motion of the water surface he devised a version of his famous optical interferometer which can measure distances as small as one-tenth the wavelength of light. The existence of tidal forces was detected and measured.

In 1939, Nörlund decided to do things on a grand scale. He mounted two vertical glass tubes on the Danish islands of Fyn and Sjaelland, some 11 miles apart, and connected them by a water-filled pipe lying on the ocean's floor. Both glass tubes were graduated in millimeters; he found that the difference in level at the two ends showed a definite periodicity of 12 hours and 25 minutes, with an amplitude of two to three millimeters. There is no doubt that Nörlund was observing the result of a tide-generating force. Again, however, the magnitude of the force was in doubt; the measured amplitude depends upon the degree of distortion of the solid earth.

How about the vertical components of the tide-generating forces? Can we go to a place where we would expect them to be maximum, and measure them directly? As we have seen earlier in the chapter, they could manifest themselves only by tiny variations in the weight of objects. The measurement of the earth's gravitational force is called *gravimetry*. Geophysicists have made it a very special science, for a variety of reasons. Variations in gravitational force over the earth's surface give valuable clues to the structure of the earth in general—to its departure from a spherical shape, for example, and to the thickness and composition of the crust. In particular, local anomalies in the gravitational field can disclose certain geological formations—for example, those associated with oil-bearing regions. The development of extremely sensitive *gravimeters* for measuring the force of gravity has thus had much encouragement both from the scientific and the commercial point of view.

Suppose you were asked to measure—very accurately —the force of gravity at a certain place. How would you do it? For the present, let's measure this force in terms of g, the acceleration a freely falling object would have in the gravitational field. By freely falling we mean motion under the influence of gravity alone; no other forces such as air friction act upon the object.

Perhaps you will say, "All right, I'll measure g directly. Let something fall in a vacuum and find its acceleration. Why not let a metal ruler drop in front of a camera, with a strobe light photographing the ruler at a rate of, say, ten times per second." This sounds good, and has in fact been done. But remember —whatever the type of experiment we do—the fantastic precision required. The vertical components of the tide-generating forces are just as small as the horizontal components; we must do our measurements to an accuracy of many decimal places! You will calibrate your ruler against the international meter. Your time intervals between the flashes must be compared with a standard-frequency radio signal. The latter is broadcast, with extreme precision, from stations such as WWV of the United States Bureau of Standards. The experiment, done with the greatest of care, can yield high accuracy in the measurement of g.

Another way may have occurred to you. Why not use a pendulum? Its time of swing, or period, depends on g. In elementary physics we learned, for example, that the period T of a simple pendulum of length L swinging through a small arc is, to a fair degree of accuracy,

$$T = 2\pi \sqrt{\frac{L}{g}}$$

For greater accuracy, we can use a complicated formula which includes various correction factors. Or—and this is more likely—we can use a device of greater sophistication called a *physical pendulum,* whose period can also be very accurately predicted as a function of *g.*

A pendulum is essentially a timing device. What we are really interested in is small changes in its period. These are the result of the tiny changes in *g* which accompany the variation in the vertical component of the tide-generating forces. Suppose we had, sitting beside the pendulum, another and equally accurate timing device *whose rate is independent of g.* We could then, by comparing the rates of the two clocks, get a direct measure of the changes in *g.* For the second clock we might use an electric one driven by the vibrations of a quartz crystal kept in a constant-temperature enclosure. Such a timing device can have high accuracy.

How about an apparatus which can measure the force of gravity *directly?* It is for such an instrument that the term *gravimeter* is ordinarily reserved. Again, the sensitivity requirement is enormous. Figure 12 shows the operating principle of the Hartley gravimeter, upon which the general design of several modern gravimeters is based. Since the vertical motion of the end of the beam is so small, enormous optical magnification is necessary. Of somewhat different design is the Hoyt gravimeter. Its central feature is a helical spring (see Plate 1). The weight is hung from this spring; any increase in gravity will cause the spring to stretch *and* to rotate. The rotation is proportional to the stretching but is much bigger, so that measurement is easier. A change in gravity of one part in ten million causes a rotation easily measured with optical amplification.

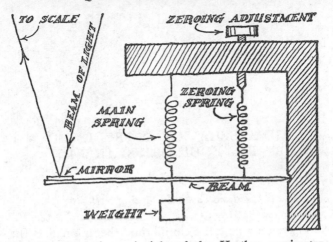

Fig. 12 Operating principle of the Hartley gravimeter.

Measurement of the vertical component of the tide-generating force has the same built-in uncertainty as does that of the horizontal component. How much does the earth itself change shape? We shall see later that the situation is not as bad as it looks now; we do know something about tides within the earth.

Chapter III

TIDAL BEHAVIOR AS PREDICTED
BY THE EQUILIBRIUM THEORY

Tides on a slowly turning earth

We have seen how the equilibrium theory predicts the bulging of the ocean's surface in those regions nearest to the moon and farthest from it. How is the existence of these bulges related to what an observer on the earth sees as tidal behavior, as the earth turns?

The phrase "as the earth turns" is extremely significant. So far in our arguments, we have in effect denied that the earth *does* rotate on its axis. For purposes of our discussion, we have stopped this rotation. But to describe what an observer sees we must obviously allow it. Can we allow it without destroying the validity of what we have said? Yes, under the following arbitrary rule: in our imagination, we must stretch out the passage of time, so that the rotation takes place extremely slowly. Let a day become a year—or better, a century. Only then can we continue our discussion on the basis of the equilibrium theory, and exclude the dynamical effects which we must take into account if we operate in real time.

Does not this necessary stretching out of time, so that every motion can be thought of as happening infinitely slowly, invalidate all conclusions based on the equilibrium theory? The answer is "no." It is true that most observed tidal phenomena differ widely from the behavior predicted purely on the basis of the equilibrium theory. Nevertheless, as we shall soon see, equilibrium theory allows us to predict the gross features (and some of the finer features) of the tides. Later, we can use dynamical concepts to modify and to expand our understanding of tidal behavior. If we were to exclude at this point any further consideration of equilibrium theory, and attack the problem on dynamical grounds alone, we should soon find ourselves mathematically in deep water, and called upon for a knowledge of fluid dynamics that only an expert in that field possesses.

We must imagine, then, an observer endowed with infinite patience, standing on an earth turning with an infinite slowness, and seeing a moon with equally slow motion in its orbit. Suppose that matters are as shown in Figure 13. Here the dashed line represents the earth. The shaded area shows the elongated figure of

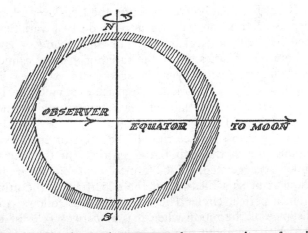

Fig. 13 As the earth turns, an observer on its surface is carried first through one "bulge" of water and then the other.

the ocean's surface due to the tide-generating forces (we still picture the earth as entirely covered with water). The drawing depicts the situation at a time when the moon is directly above the earth's equator; the earth-moon line is perpendicular to the earth's axis. If the observer himself is on the equator, then as the earth turns it will carry him first through one bulge of water and then through the other. He will see two tides a day essentially equal in amount, and they will be of maximum height since he passes through the top of each bulge. Tides which occur twice a day are called *semi-diurnal* tides. If the observer is not on the equator but somewhat to the north or south he will, as the figure shows, pass through only part of the bulge. Obviously, he will see a smaller range in the height of the tide. The tide will still be semi-diurnal.

Periodicities

If our patient observer measures the tides over a long period of time he will see a good deal of variation, and he will find that most of the changes have certain periodicities. Why the variations? They cannot be connected with dynamic effects, for we are still imagining that all motions take place extremely slowly. The reasons are several; some are easy to understand, and others will need some thought.

In Figure 14 we see the elliptic orbit of the moon around the earth, with the eccentricity of the ellipse much exaggerated. The term *eccentricity* can be thought of as a measure of the departure of the orbit from a perfect circle. The departure is as follows: the distance of the moon when it is at *perigee* (closest to the earth) is about 222,000 miles, and at *apogee* (farthest from the earth) it is about 253,000 miles. The period from one perigee to the next, known as the

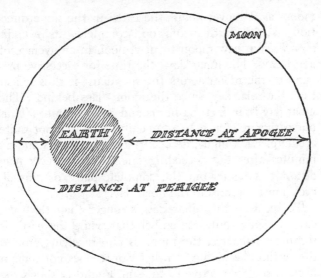

Fig. 14 Orbit of the moon around the earth.

anomalistic month, requires 27.55 days. The inverse cube law for the tide-generating forces means that even small changes in distance can have observable effects, and we do see a tidal variation with this periodicity.

In a similar way, that part of the tide-generating force produced by the sun is affected by the eccentricity of the earth's orbit. Here the corresponding periodicity is the *anomalistic year*. It is slightly longer than the "true," or *sidereal*, year, because the line connecting earth and sun at perigee progresses round the earth's orbit by an average of 11 seconds of arc per year.

Lunar versus solar day

So far we have said nothing of a much larger and extremely important cause of variation in the tides. It results from the combined effects of the earth's and moon's respective revolutions in their orbits. The moon, as it moves about the earth in the same direction as the earth's rotation, completes its *synodic month* from new moon to new moon in an average of 29.53 days. The lunar day—the time for successive passages of the moon across the meridian—is thus longer than the solar day, since the moon "lags behind." The lunar day is, in fact, 24 hours and 50.47 minutes. Thus our earlier reference to semi-daily tides was not quite accurate. Each high tide occurs about 12 hours and 25 minutes after the preceding one. (Local effects may distort this figure, but the complete daily, or *diurnal*, cycle must conform to the lunar day.)

To see why the lunar day is longer than the solar day, you need only remember that while the earth is turning on its axis, the moon is also revolving around the earth. The moon, in other words, does not remain fixed in the sky relative to the sun. Figure 15 shows the

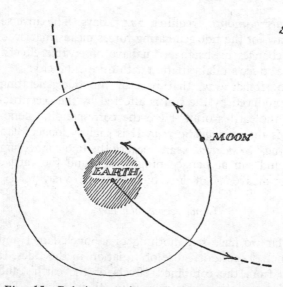

Fig. 15   Relative motions of the earth and the moon.

moon moving about the earth while the earth follows its own orbit about the sun. (The moon's period of rotation on its own axis is equal to the period of its revolution around the earth, so that it always presents the same face to us.) The drawing is a little idealized, since it is not the earth's center but rather the center of gravity of the earth-moon system which traces out the smooth orbit around the sun. The center of the earth must therefore follow a somewhat wavy line— but the waviness is, of course, very small. After all, the distance from the earth's center to the earth-moon center of gravity is only 2900 miles. The waviness of the moon's path as it also goes around the sun is, of course, much greater. This makes the following statement hard to believe when you first hear it—but it's true: the path of the moon is always *concave toward the sun!* The reason: the speed of the earth in its orbit is more than 30 times as great as that of the moon around the earth. The resulting path of the moon deviates only very slightly from the earth's orbit. All of which means that the size of the moon's orbit in Figure 15 is enormously exaggerated. This is the trouble with many astronomical diagrams; if you draw things to scale, you can't show what you want to show!

But we have been getting away from our main point, which was to show how the moon's motion lengthens the lunar day. In Figure 16 the earth, moon, and sun are shown in *conjunction*—i.e., they are all approximately in the same line, with the moon between the earth and the sun. (If they were exactly in line, the moon would be eclipsing the sun.) Two conjunctions are drawn; position (2) of the moon has occurred 29.53 days—i.e., a synodic month—after position (1). The moon therefore moves

$$\frac{360°}{29.53 \text{ days}} = 12.2°$$

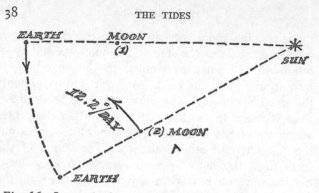

Fig. 16 Interval of one synodic month.

to the eastward of the sun each day. If in the synodic month there are 29.53 solar days, there must be 28.53 lunar days, since the moon during the synodic month makes a complete revolution to the eastward from the sun to the sun again, thereby losing one entire revolution. The length of the lunar day must therefore be

$$\frac{29.53}{28.53} \times 24 \text{ hours} = 24 \text{ hours}, 50.47 \text{ minutes}$$

So we have accounted exactly for the observed lag in the semi-diurnal tide!

It must be added that though the retardation of the moon's transit *averages* 50.47 minutes per day, the figure can actually range from 38 to 66 minutes. Variations in the rate of the moon's motion because of its elliptical orbit and because of the inclination of its orbit to that of the earth account for the difference.

Combined action of lunar and solar tides

When the moon is full (in *opposition*) or new (in *conjunction*), the tide-generating forces are at their maximum. At these times the earth, moon, and sun are all approximately in line (see Figure 17); the tidal effects of sun and moon are therefore additive. Ex-

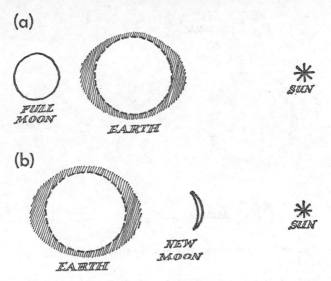

Fig. 17 The moon in opposition (a) and conjunction (b).

tremely high tidal ranges (the *spring* tides) should be experienced on both sides of the earth at fortnightly intervals. Actually, because of effects we have not yet considered, spring tides lag somewhat behind the times of conjunction and opposition.

In Figure 18 we see what happens when sun and moon are in *quadrature*. Here we have the situation of minimum tidal range—the neap tides. It is hardly correct to imply, as some people do, that the sun and moon are now pulling against each other, in the sense of direct opposition. This can never occur. Rather, as we see from the diagram, the tide-generating forces are operating at right angles to each other; we say that they are 90 degrees out of phase.

It is interesting that during winter in the Northern Hemisphere the sun is at perigee. For a large number of earth dwellers, then, winter is slightly less severe

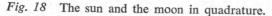

Fig. 18 The sun and the moon in quadrature.

than it might otherwise be. In terms of the tides, it follows that their range at conjunction or opposition is greater, and at quadratures less, than in the summer.

Another interesting point: every month the moon, at perigee, raises greater tides than two weeks later or before. Thus the two highest ranges cannot follow one another in two succeeding spring tides.

What happens when the moon is in some intermediate position between quadrature and conjunction or opposition? Analysis shows that for the moon in its first or third quarters the tidal crest forms *behind* the moon. Consequently an observer on a rotating earth will see the tidal crest occur *before* the moon passes the meridian. Figure 19a will make clear this statement, which at first reading may look contradictory. During the second and fourth quarters, Figure 19b, high water occurs *after* the moon's transit, and we speak of a "lagging" tide. In each diagram the amount of leading and lagging has been exaggerated for clarity.

If you look at Figure 20, you will find a summary of

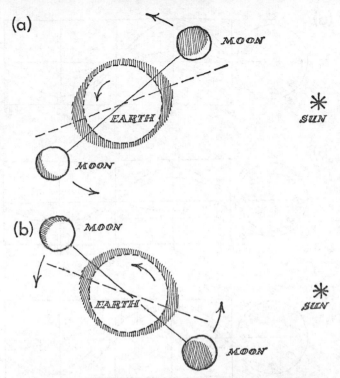

Fig. 19 (a and b) Positions of tidal bulge when the moon is intermediate between quadrature and conjunction or opposition. The corresponding phases of the moon are drawn approximately as they would look to an observer on the earth.

what we've been saying about the combined action of the lunar and solar tides. It is valid for an observer at the equator. Here we have graphs in which the dotted line represents the height of the solar tide, the dashed line that of the lunar tide, and the solid line the combination of the two tides. The graphs extend over half a lunar day, with hours plotted horizontally. In each case the circle at the left shows the relative position of

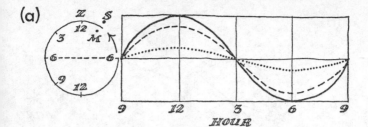

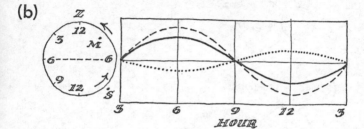

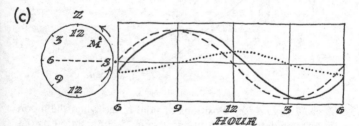

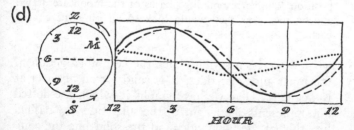

Fig. 20 Combined action of lunar and solar tides. (After Bidlingmaier, Samml. Meereskunde, No. 5, 1908.)

the sun and moon. The top, Z, of the circle, is the *zenith*, i.e., the point directly over the observer, and the observer's horizon is indicated by the horizontal dashed line. The symbol S stands for the sun and M for the moon, and the numerals within the circles represent the time of day or night.

Part (a) shows conditions at new moon. At twelve o'clock both moon and sun will be at Z, and the water level is considerably higher than for the lunar tide alone. We have a spring tide. But if in this figure we move M to the opposite side of the circle, we have a full moon and also a spring tide; tidal conditions are the same, and there is no need to draw another graph. Part (b) makes clear the situation for neap tides. By the time the moon has reached the zenith, the sun will just be rising at six o'clock; they are in quadrature. The solar and lunar tidal effects are opposing each other. The rise and the fall of the sea are small.

In Part (c) phase relations are a little more complicated. Here we are halfway between spring and neap tides. The sun is just rising at six o'clock and the moon is three hours ahead of it. When the moon is overhead at nine o'clock in the morning, the sun still has three hours to rise until noon. Thus the lunar tide reaches a peak three hours before that of the sun. The position of the dotted and dashed lines produces the result shown.

Finally, in Part (d) we are halfway between neap tide and spring tide. When the moon reaches the zenith at 3:00 A.M. it will still be nine hours until the sun is overhead. The result is apparent.

Declination

Perhaps we had better pause for a moment to summarize our predictions so far about tidal behavior. We expect a semi-diurnal tide at intervals of 12 hours and

25 minutes. Furthermore, we have found three reasons to expect variations in the height of this tide: the varying distance of the moon in its orbit, the varying distance of the sun in its orbit, and most importantly, the changing positions of the sun and moon relative to each other. The first of these variations has a period of 27½ days, the second of about a year, and the third of about a fortnight.

But our patient observer would notice additional variations in the tide, each with a characteristic periodicity. Where can they arise? Surely as a result of some oversimplification in our description of the earth-moon-sun system. This naïveté is not hard to find; we have assumed so far that the moon's orbit lies in the earth's *equatorial plane,* a plane defined by the equatorial ring of the earth. For someone on the equator, then, we are saying that the moon when it crosses the meridian is always straight overhead! And we have implicitly assumed the same of the sun, so that the plane defined by the earth's path in its journey around the sun, the plane of the moon's orbit around the earth, and the earth's equatorial plane, are one and the same.

We must now face the fact that these are indeed three different planes in space. The earth's axis is tilted, so much that the equatorial plane makes an angle of 23½ degrees with the plane of the earth's orbit. Furthermore, the plane of the moon's orbit is at an angle of 5 degrees to the earth's orbit. We cannot continue our discussion without first pointing out the geometrical situation relating to these statements.

Figure 21 makes clear that the earth's axis maintains a constant direction in space. This direction is tilted at an angle of 23½ degrees with respect to a line drawn perpendicular to the plane of the earth's orbit. The most apparent result of this tilt: summer and winter! But we are not here concerned with the weather. We

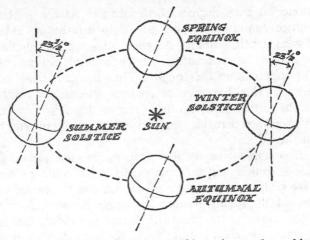

Fig. 21 Inclination of the earth's axis to the orbital plane.

want to relate the direction of the axis to tidal phenomena.

Four positions of the earth are shown; two of them are the *equinoxes*. At these times, the earth's equatorial plane passes through the sun. Night and day are of equal length (neglecting the effect of atmospheric refraction), and on the equator the sun is straight overhead at noon. The other two positions are the *solstices*. Here the sun achieves its maximum *declination*, or latitude at which it is directly overhead at noon. At the summer solstice the declination is 23½ degrees north in the Northern Hemisphere; if you are at that latitude, you will see the sun straight over you. For the winter solstice, you will have to travel to a latitude of 23½ degrees south to see the sun straight overhead.

Certain facts are immediately obvious. At the summer solstice (about June 21) the line joining the centers of the earth and sun penetrates the earth's

surface at 23½ degrees north latitude. At the winter
solstice (about December 21) it penetrates at 23½
degrees south latitude. At the spring and autumnal
equinoxes (approximately March 21 and September
21) it penetrates the equator. Thus the center line of
the solar tidal forces varies 47 degrees north and south
on the earth's surface as the year goes through its cycle.
We shall see that this variation has an important effect
on the tides.

Meanwhile what about the moon, the more powerful
tide-generating object? The plane of its orbit, as we
have said, makes an angle of 5 degrees with respect to
that of the earth. Because this angle is so small, the
moon moves north and south during the month about
as much as does the sun during the year. A phenomenon known as the regression of the moon's nodes
introduces a little variety and a new periodicity, however. The intersection of the plane of the moon's orbit
with the plane of the earth's orbit rotates; a complete
revolution takes 18.6 years. Thus there are times (it
occurred in 1950) that the moon's declination reaches
23½ degrees plus 5 degrees, or 28½ degrees. At these
times the center line of the lunar tide-generating force
is varying north and south on the earth's surface by
57 degrees during the month. After 9.3 years, however,
the maximum declination of the moon is 23½ degrees
minus 5 degrees, or 18½ degrees. Then the north-
south variation during the month is only 37 degrees.

Precession of the equinoxes

While we're discussing the earth-sun and earth-
moon spatial relations, we might as well go whole-hog
and mention another matter that has a bearing upon
tidal behavior. This is the *precession of the equinoxes*,
a term used by astronomers to describe the fact that
the axis of rotation of the earth does not continue

pointing in the same direction, but slowly changes. Those who have had some introduction to physics may be puzzled by this fact. They may say, "If the earth is rotating it has angular momentum about its axis of rotation. And angular momentum of an object stays the same (is conserved) unless some outside torque acts on the object. Now angular momentum is a vector quantity—i.e., it has both magnitude and direction. Even if you keep the *magnitude* the same—which means keeping the rotational speed constant and therefore the length of the day unchanged—you still can't change the *direction* of the earth's axis of rotation. That is, you can't change it without applying some external torque. If the earth is a sphere and therefore symmetrical, how is the sun—or moon, or anything else—going to exert a twist on it?"

A good question. The only flaw in the argument: the earth is not a perfect sphere. It bulges around the middle, and therein lies the source of the torque. In Figure 22 we see the earth with its middle-age spread considerably exaggerated. All parts of the bulge are attracted to the moon—but not equally. A mass on the far side is pulled by a force F_1, which is less than the

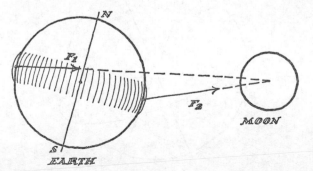

Fig. 22 Torque exerted by the moon on the bulge of the earth.

force F_2 on an equal mass on the near side. So there is a torque trying to "straighten up" the earth's axis and make it perpendicular to the earth-moon line. Now the earth is just a big gyroscope, or spinning top. Nothing is more perverse than a gyroscope. If you try to tip it in a certain direction, it refuses to go. Rather, its axis of rotation moves slowly at right angles to the way you wish. If you want to know the reason for this you'll have to look it up in a physics book. The explanation is not hard to see, but it's time-consuming.

So the earth, subject to a torque from the moon—and from the sun, also, but the sun merely adds to the whole effect—does change the direction of its axis of rotation. The axis slowly traces out a cone of half-angle 23½ degrees (see Figure 23). Slowly, because a

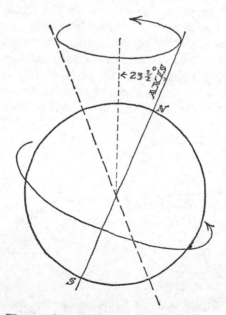

Fig. 23 The earth's precession.

complete revolution takes about 26,000 years. To you and me this may seem quite a while, but in terms of astronomical and geological time it is a rapid motion.

Figure 24 shows where the pole was and will be at various times. If you face north, the precessional mo-

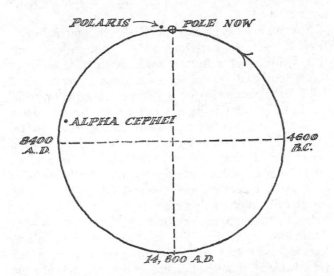

Fig. 24 Precessional motion of the celestial pole.

tion of the north celestial pole (the point where the earth's axis pierces the imaginary "celestial sphere") is counterclockwise. The pole is at present only about 1 degree in angle from Polaris, the "North Star." In the year 2100 the pole will be only ½ degree from Polaris. But in A.D. 7500, it will be 28 degrees from Polaris! Any mariner who then tries to steer by Polaris will be out of luck. Fortunately, the star Alpha Cephei will at that time be so close to the north celestial pole that it can be called the North Star.

Effect of declination

We have been seeing how, for various reasons, the tide-generating forces are continually changing their direction with respect to the axis of the earth. And we have found that with each effect there is a corresponding periodicity.

Now we need to go back and ask a fundamental question. If the tide-generating body is not in line with the earth's equator, but has some declination north or south, how will this affect what our observer sees? Let's first assume that he is still on the equator, waiting to tell us about the rise and fall of the tide. How he does this is something of a question, since, as you will recall, we imagine the earth to be entirely covered with water. Perhaps we can think of him as perched on a long telephone pole driven into the bed of the ocean, and measuring the rise and fall of the sea by bands painted on the pole.

If the tide-generating body—say the moon—has declination zero, i.e., lies in the equatorial plane, then as the earth turns the observer will note the tidal behavior described earlier in this chapter. On the other hand, if the moon is in line with the earth's pole, so that the declination is 90 degrees, he will see no tide at all. What will he observe if the declination has some intermediate value? It turns out that there are some very interesting consequences.

Figure 25 shows the two hemispheres of the earth at a time when the moon's declination is 28 degrees south. It follows that for some point on the earth at latitude 28 degrees south, the moon will be straight overhead. The point is marked on the diagram by a small black spot. The position diametrically opposite this spot on the other side of the earth at latitude 28 degrees north is marked in a similar way. An attempt is made in the

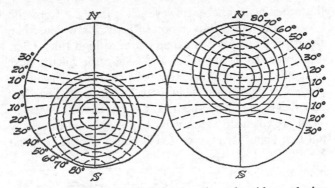

Fig. 25 Position of tidal bulges when the tide-producing body has a declination of 28°.

diagram to show the corresponding bulges of the ocean. The lines which are roughly circular represent contours of equal tidal height. On a model globe one could draw them as true circles—as, of course, they are. But to go from a diagram on a globe to one on paper is to change from a three-dimensional to a two-dimensional representation, with accompanying distortion. You have already met this difficulty if you have tried to draw world maps.

The smaller the circle, the higher the tide in that region. The tops of the bulges are at the black spot. Crossing the circles are dashed lines of constant latitude. The corresponding values of the latitudes are given at the edges of the diagram.

Our observer on the telephone pole at the equator will now report that he still sees two equal tides a day, but that their height is less. True enough; as he is carried along by the rotation of the earth, he no longer passes through the tops of the bulges. Now let's move him to a latitude of say, 28 degrees—north or south, it doesn't matter which. We'll watch his progress across the two hemispheres. His parallel of latitude, on one hemisphere, cuts very close to the top of the bulge. On the other hemisphere, however, it passes far from the top of the bulge. His report: "First I saw low tide; about six hours later the water rose to high tide. Then low water again. But when the time came for the next high tide, there was a pretty poor showing. The water reached a maximum height at the proper time, but that height was very small. What happened, anyway?" Well, we've already seen what happened, and can easily tell him about it. Figure 26 will help with the explana-

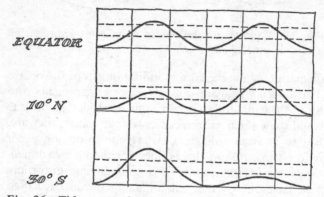

Fig. 26 Tides at various latitudes when the declination of the tide-producing body is 28°.

tion. Here are shown varying heights of tide, for three different latitudes, when the moon has a declination of 28 degrees. Why the observer reported as he did is evident.

We see that the range of two successive tides is in general not the same. This is called the *diurnal inequality*, and is of great importance in tidal theory. It embodies a periodicity of one day—i.e., the entire cycle takes one lunar day and is called the *diurnal tide*. Here is another variation to add to our list of tidal periodicities, and it can be, as you see, a significant one. In a later chapter we shall discuss tides as they actually occur in various parts of the world. There are locations where there is only one tide a day—the diurnal one! The semi-diurnal tide is suppressed by local geographical peculiarities.

So far, in talking about the motion of the tide-producing object, we have discussed nothing of the results of periodic changes in declination. Some pages earlier, however, we prepared ourselves for such a discussion. It is obvious now that a change in declination produces a change in tidal behavior. Both sun and moon contribute, of course, as they move from the equator into the Northern and Southern Hemispheres. For the moon the declinational oscillation is completed in a *tropical month* of 27.32 days (a tropical month is the time between two successive passages of the moon through the earth's equatorial plane). The period of the resulting declinational inequality in the tide is just one-half of this, however, or 13.66 days. The reason: the inequality depends only on the absolute amount of the declination, and not upon its sign.

Changes in declination introduce large variations in the diurnal inequality. Figure 27 is an example; it shows a record of total rise and fall at San Francisco. For the upper curve the moon was over the equator. For the lower, the moon had its maximum declination in the north, some seven days later. The difference in the diurnal inequality is impressive. This record is, of course, descriptive of a local situation only. Other regions might exhibit two curves quite different in shape from those shown. The point is, however, that everywhere there would be a *difference* in the diurnal inequalities between the upper and lower curves.

The greatest semi-diurnal range of tide will occur when the moon is on the equator; the smallest, when the moon has its greatest declination. This variation is called, for the moon, the *lunar fortnightly tide*. For the sun, the corresponding effect is the *solar semiannual*

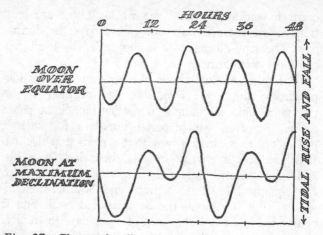

Fig. 27 Change in diurnal inequality due to different declinations of the moon.

tide. Note that the lunar fortnightly variation has nothing directly to do with the changing phase of the moon with respect to the sun. The changing phase, which results in springs and neaps, has a periodicity of half a *synodic month*, or 14.76 days.

You may be interested to know what conditions give rise to the greatest possible astronomical tide-generating forces. They occur when, all at the same time, the sun is in perigee, the sun and moon are in conjunction or opposition, and *both sun and moon have zero declination.* This combination of circumstances happens about every 1600 years. Astronomers have calculated that it occurred about 250 B.C. and A.D. 1400, and will happen again around A.D. 3300.

Summary

By now the reader may be somewhat bewildered by the complexity of the variations in the tide-generating forces. The rotating earth is subject to gravitational forces from two objects, the sun and the moon. (We have not mentioned gravitational forces due to the other planets; their effect is utterly negligible.) With respect to the earth, and with respect to each other, the sun and moon move in a most complicated way. The saving grace is that each aspect of each motion has a corresponding periodicity; the tidal variations can be related to these periodicities. It will be of help if we summarize some of our discussion in the light of this statement.

1. The equilibrium tide is composed of constant *terms*. There are, for example, semi-diurnal oscillations and diurnal oscillations.

2. Variations in amplitude are related to:
   a. Changes in declination of the tide-generating object.
   b. Changes in distance of the tide-generating object.
   c. Changes in relative position of the sun and moon.

The accompanying Table I lists some of the more important terms in tidal behavior. Actually, the list could go on for some pages. We have discussed in this chapter only the general aspects of what, in the equilibrium theory, produces the observed tides. We have related these ideas to some of the more important periodicities. But because of the complication of the whole situation, there are many more periodicities which we have not even mentioned. Fortunately, their contribution is usually small and can be neglected except when an extremely precise calculation of tidal behavior is carried out.

TABLE I

Effect	Period	Related Astronomical Cycle	Cause
Semi-diurnal	12 hr., 25 min.	Time between upper and lower transits of moon	Rotation of earth
Diurnal	24 hr., 50 min.	Time between succeeding upper or lower transits of moon	Rotation of earth and declination of sun and moon
Interval between spring tides	14.76 days (average)	Time from conjunction to opposition or vice versa	Phase relation between sun and moon
Lunar fortnightly	13.66 days	Time for moon to change declination from zero to maximum and back to zero	Varying declination of moon
Anomalistic month	27.55 days	Time for moon to go from perigee to perigee	Ellipticity of moon's orbit
Solar semi-annual	182.6 days	Time for sun to change declination from zero to maximum and back to zero	Varying declination of sun
Anomalistic year	365.26 days	Time for earth to go from perigee to perigee	Ellipticity of earth's orbit

Chapter IV

DYNAMICAL THEORY

Weakness of the equilibrium theory

On a recent evening, the author was sloshing along in his rubber boots over an exposed tidal flat. The moon was full and directly overhead, and by its light it was easy to see mussels clinging, as is their habit, to rocks uncovered only at low water.

What is inherent in the above statement? On the face of it, nothing very exciting. But stop to think a moment. Would not some people say it implies a complete breakdown of the equilibrium theory of the tides?

The locale was Penobscot Bay in Maine; spring tides here may easily have a range of 10 or 11 feet. According to the equilibrium theory, the author on the tidal flat should not have been hiking but drowning! For do not the tide-generating forces create a tidal bulge on the earth-moon line at the time of opposition? Equilibrium theory says so.

Equilibrium theory on this point, at least, is obviously entirely wrong. And yet the calculation of the tide-producing forces is based on the most precise astronomical data. The relative motions of the earth, moon, and sun are extremely complicated, but they are known to great accuracy. Given a modern electronic computer, then, there is no difficulty in determining these forces and their variation with time to almost any degree of refinement.

You remember that in the previous chapter we made a rather indigestible assumption—that everything was moving infinitely slowly. We did it, we said, to eliminate any effect of inertia from our considerations. Obviously, the presence of the tidal bulges implies motion of large water masses. Mass, in turn, implies inertial effects if accelerations are involved. And certainly on a rotating earth, with tide-generating objects which are themselves moving in complicated paths, all sorts of accelerations are going to exist.

We were very inconsistent. We did not rule that water has no mass, because without mass it could suffer no gravitational attraction. Rather, we gave it *gravitational mass* but denied that it has *inertial mass!*

Now the concept *mass* is a subtle thing. This is not the place for a physical and philosophical discussion of the term. We can say, however, that an object has mass ("gravitational mass") if it has weight—i.e., if it experiences a force when in a gravitational field. We can also say that the object has mass ("inertial mass") if a force is required to accelerate or decelerate it; that is, if it exhibits inertia. There is no *a priori* reason to say that these two kinds of mass are necessarily the same. Nevertheless, experiments of the greatest delicacy (the most famous being that of Eötvös) have shown that gravitational mass and inertial mass are directly proportional to each other.

We can no longer profitably maintain the fiction that water has no inertia. The presence of inertia must be at least one of the effects that undermine the predictions of the equilibrium theory. (Our feeling is strengthened when we notice that the equilibrium theory does indeed predict correctly the very long-period components of the tide. Here inertial effects would be minimal.)

It is easy to attack the equilibrium theory: high water can come at the wrong time, as we have just seen; the range of tide is not usually as predicted; the observed diurnal inequality often bears no relation to the theory (in some places the tide which should be the greater is the less). But the equilibrium theory has one great virtue: it unreels a thread of truth which weaves its way through almost all tidal phenomena. We have seen that the theory is essentially one of periodicities. So, too, do our observations show periodicities—in general, the same ones. If the actual times when things happen, or their magnitudes, disagree with the theory, let's see what extensions of the theory are possible with the hope of patching things up.

Does this offend your sensibilities? You may say, "Surely science must operate in a less messy way than this. If a theory isn't very good, forget the whole thing and start afresh with an entirely new one." In point of fact, however, science does ordinarily progress in this "messy way." Almost never is a theory entirely discarded, for never is every part of it wrong. So we make new assumptions and build them into an extended and (if they work) better theory. The process is, of course, never-ending. There is no perfect theory; each new one is simply a step on the path toward still more successful theories.

With the tides we have in truth no choice. No one has been able to conceive of a purely dynamical theory which could directly relate the tide-generating forces to the actual tides of the world. There are far too many variables—the complicated shapes of the oceans, their varying depths, the subtle effects which a fluid experiences when it moves over the surface of a rotating sphere.

Concept of the tidal wave

What, then, shall we do next? We had better super-
impose on the equilibrium theory some actual dynamic
conditions. Long years ago, in fact, this work was begun
for us by the great French scientist and mathemati-
cian Laplace. He was the first to realize the full difficulty of the problem; this difficulty, he saw, was inherent in the earth's rotation.

What Laplace said was essentially this: let us talk in
terms of *tidal waves* rather than bulges of water. The
waves are induced by the rhythmical horizontal components of the forces of gravitation—and have the
same periods as these forces. So the problem of the
tides is a problem of the motion of a fluid. This motion is, of course, modified by the size and shape of
the ocean basins, by their depth, by friction, and by
effects—such as the Coriolis force—arising from the
earth's rotation.

We must make clear at the outset that when we use
the term *tidal wave* it has nothing directly to do with
the catastrophic "tidal waves" dear to the newspaper
headline writers. Such waves are either *tsunamis*
generated by earthquakes, or *storm surges*. A *tsunami*
is created when a subsea surface moves quickly because
of seismic activity and communicates its motion to a
mass of water. A storm surge is a large rise in water
level due to the action of violent winds, accompanied
perhaps by a traveling area of low barometric pressure.*

* For a fascinating account of these phenomena and
their sometimes catastrophic results, see Bascom, Willard, *Waves and Beaches*, Science Study Series, 1964, and
Leet, L. Don, *Causes of Catastrophe*, McGraw-Hill, 1948.

The general notion of wave

What is a *wave*? We had better refresh our minds on some important points. Figure 28 shows a transverse wave, such as would be produced in a stretched rope if one end were moved up and down with a regular

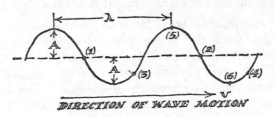

Fig. 28 Transverse wave.

motion. The *displacement* of any point on the rope is its vertical distance from the center line. The maximum value of the displacement we call the *amplitude*, the distance A in the diagram. We see that the shape of the wave repeats itself in a distance λ, the *wavelength*. Speaking in different terms, the wavelength is the distance from one point in the wave to the next point having the same *phase*. Between these two points is "one complete wave." From one crest to the next is, for example, one wavelength. So is the distance from one trough to the next, or from point (1) to point (2). We have now, in fact, also defined the term *phase*. It describes what a particle of the rope is doing. If two pendulums having the same period swing in the same direction at the same time, we say that they are in the *same phase* or *in phase*. If they start together but swing in opposite directions, we say that they are in the *opposite phase* or *out of phase*. In the diagram, points (1) and (2) are in the same phase, as are points

(3) and (4). Points (5) and (6), on the other hand, are out of phase.

The whole wave propagates (moves forward) with a speed *v*. Such a wave is called a *progressive wave*. The number of complete waves passing any given place per second is the frequency of the wave. The time for one complete wave to pass is the *period T*. From the definitions of these quantities, it is obvious that $f = \frac{1}{T}$, and also that $v = \lambda f$. If the rope that we have used as an example is tied at one end to a rigid support, and if we continue to agitate the other end, we get a new and interesting phenomenon. The rope rises and falls without the waves seeming to travel one way or the other. These are called *stationary* or *standing* waves. What is happening? The wave is being reflected at the fixed end, and on the rope are therefore two waves of the same frequency and amplitude traveling in opposite directions. The waves on the strings of a violin are standing waves, as are the sound waves in an organ pipe.

If we watch the rope closely when it is vibrating as a standing wave, we see that there are certain places, called *nodes*, at which there is little or no motion. Halfway between the nodes, however, are regions of maximum motion called *anti-nodes*. Nodes (N) and anti-nodes (A-N) are spaced one-half wavelength apart, as we see in Figure 29.

For our discussion we have chosen a *transverse* wave,

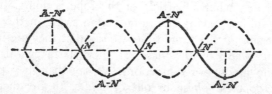

Fig. 29   Standing wave.

one in which the particles of the propagating medium vibrate at right angles to the direction in which the wave is going. Sound waves in gases, on the other hand, are propagated as *longitudinal* waves. The wave motion consists of back-and-forth motions of the air molecules in the same direction as that of the wave itself.

You realize, of course, that in no type of wave motion do the particles of the medium themselves move along with the wave. On the average they stay in the same place, and propagate the wave by communicating their own vibrations to the neighboring particles.

Now let's talk of water waves. Are they longitudinal or transverse? Neither. What sort of motion, then, does a "hunk of water" execute? Or better, how would we see a floating cork move as the waves pass by? "Up and down," you might say, but you would be wrong. If you watch closely, you see that the cork executes a simultaneous up-and-down, to-and-fro motion. When a crest is approaching, the cork is rising. On the crest, it moves forward in the direction of the waves. But soon the crest passes by and the cork falls. When it is in the trough of the wave it is moving backward opposite to the wave velocity, at a speed equal to that which it had when it was on the crest.

The cork, in other words, traces out a roughly circular orbit which is completed once every period. The diameter of the orbit is obviously equal to the wave height, or vertical distance from trough to crest. The cork is simply following the motion of the water particles on the surface. What about water particles below the surface? They also are moving in orbits, but the diameter of the orbit decreases rapidly with depth. A submarine does not have to submerge far to escape the effects of the worst ocean storms.

Suppose the waves are impinging on the vertical face of a sea wall and therefore being reflected. We now have the necessary condition for a standing wave. Next time you are on a pier or jetty, watch for standing waves. They are easy to recognize, for they look very strange. The waves don't seem to travel anywhere; they just go up and down. A crest becomes a trough and then a crest again; here is an anti-node. Halfway between are the *nodal lines*, where a floating object is almost undisturbed.

There is a convenient division of water waves into two classes, deep-water or *surface* waves and shallow-water or *long* waves. If the depth to the bottom of the ocean is less than half a wavelength, let's call the water shallow. Otherwise, we'll call it deep. Thus we make depth a relative term, depending on the size of the waves we are talking about. In shallow regions no vertical motion of the water particles can exist at the bottom. Thus the character of the waves is modified. Here the motion can be only back and forth. The orbits which are circular at the surface become progressively more elliptical with increasing depth. At the bottom the ellipses degenerate into horizontal lines. We see that waves in shallow water essentially consist of forward and backward shifts of whole water masses. The speed of the wave, as we might expect, depends upon the depth. It does not depend on the wavelength.

Surface waves are the sort of wave we originally talked about. Their speed is dependent on wavelength but independent of depth.

The canal model

Our discussion at the moment is pointed toward the understanding of a particular kind of wave—the tidal wave. Such a wave is of very long period, the period of the corresponding tide-generating force. The wavelength is correspondingly extremely great. *All tidal waves are therefore long, or shallow-water, waves.* For them, even the deepest ocean is "shallow." If the rotation of the earth is disregarded (soon we shall be considering its effect), their speed in water of depth h is $v = \sqrt{gh}$, where g is the acceleration of gravity. The speed of long waves can be enormous. Imagine a canal encircling the equator. If this canal is 5 kilometers in depth, and if some terrific impulse should generate a great wave in the canal, the wave would travel at a speed of

$$v = \sqrt{gh} = \sqrt{9.8 \text{ meters/sec}^2 \times 5000 \text{ meters}}$$
$$= 222 \text{ meters/sec}$$

or 800 kilometers (500 miles) per hour. For a deeper canal the speed would be even greater, of course.

This is a good point at which to make still another classification of waves into two types, *free* and *forced*. A free wave, once generated, travels at its own pace undisturbed by external factors, just as a pendulum swings with its own characteristic period once you give it a push. In general, however, waves—and in particular tidal waves—are produced by the continuous action of external forces. Such waves are forced waves. The situation is like that of a pendulum when you push it at a rate which is not necessarily the same as its natural period of vibration. The pendulum has no choice; it must swing in time with the force you apply; it is a forced oscillation.

Suppose our equatorial canal is 13.7 miles deep. The corresponding speed of a wave is 1040 miles per hour. Such a wave would go all the way around the earth in exactly one day. Now the earth turns with respect to the sun in one day. Let the sun be directly over the equator. Thus the solar tidal influence (to simplify our argument, let's "abolish" the moon for the moment) travels over the surface of the earth at exactly 1040 miles per hour. The free wave in the canal is just keeping pace with the sun. Since the sun's gravitational force is continually being exerted, we would expect two tremendous wave crests to build up on opposite sides of the earth. We have, in fact, a condition of *resonance* referred to in Chapter 1. Could there be a condition of resonance if the canal encircles the earth at some northern or southern latitude? Yes, if the canal had an appropriate depth, so that a free wave in it would have the same period as the earth's rotation.

The condition of resonance is, you might say, an accidental one. A free wave will have a period depending on the ocean depth. The period of the tide-generating force and therefore of the forced wave is always fixed, however. It may be greater or less than the period of the free wave. What is the result? How does the water behave in these different circumstances? We can make some sense out of it with a mechanical analogy.

Suppose I attach a weight to the bottom of a fairly flexible coil spring, and hold the top of the spring in my hand (Figure 30). Now I move my hand up and down at various rates—the forcing frequency. I soon find a rhythm in which the weight oscillates through a very large amplitude. This is the resonant condition; I am moving my hand at just the natural frequency of vibration of the system.

Now I move my hand more slowly. The forcing period is larger than the free period. I notice that the motion of the weight stays *in phase* with the motion of my hand. It "copies." When my hand is rising, so is the weight. Both reach the top (and bottom) of their respective excursions at the same time.

Suppose I move my hand faster than the free period. I notice something very peculiar; the motion of the weight is in exactly the opposite phase to that of my hand. When my hand is all the way up, the weight is at the bottom, and vice versa. *The motion is exactly inverted with respect to the force creating the motion.*

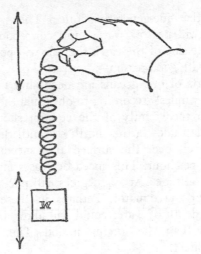

Fig. 30 Oscillations of a weight suspended on a spring.

All this behavior is predicted for any vibrating system when you set up the situation mathematically. If you want to see how that is done, a good text in mechanics will show you.

Perhaps by now you can guess what the general course of our argument is to be. Imagine an earth covered with water. The water is contained, however, in adjacent canals encircling the earth. Each canal follows a parallel of latitude. Consider first the canal around the equator. If it is more than 13.7 miles deep the free wave will travel faster than the sun. Here we have, then, the situation that the period of the tide-generating force is greater than the free period of the wave. The force and the wave will be in phase; high water will be directly beneath the sun. Such a tide is called *direct*.

But if the canal is less than 13.7 miles deep, the wave period is the greater, and the wave is in the opposite phase to the tide-generating force. Thus, under the sun there will be *low water*—and correspondingly on the opposite side of the earth the tide will be low. This is called—with good reason—an *inverted* tide.

Now parts of our oceans are deep—but nowhere as deep as 13.7 miles! According to our canal theory, then, all tides in the vicinity of the equator should be inverted. In latitudes farther north or south the tidal influence travels over the surface at a speed less than 1040 miles per hour. This speed decreases rapidly with increasing latitude. At 60 degrees latitude it is only half that at the equator. Perhaps in these canals a reasonable depth of water could still allow a free wave period less than the forcing period. Then the tide would be direct.

According to this argument, we could have inverted tides in the equatorial canals and direct tides in the canals at the higher latitudes. At some critical latitude there would be a canal in a resonant condition.

All this business of canals seems highly artificial, and the author would be the first to agree. But we have already gotten something of great value. We have seen how, by admitting the existence of inertial effects, there can be tides out of phase with the tide-generating forces—a matter of common observation. To this extent we have "patched up" the equilibrium theory. (The moon's effect was neglected in favor of the sun's. The argument was simpler for a tide-producing object "making a revolution about the earth" in exactly one day. You see, though, that the argument is no different for the moon. The canal depths would simply be somewhat less. An additional complication is the changing declination of sun and moon. This introduces mathematical difficulties but doesn't change the general tenor of the argument.)

Geostrophic effects

The next step is to remove the canals by taking away the walls which separate them. We now have, as before, merely an earth covered with water. What role did the canal walls play? They restricted all waves—and currents, if any—to a purely east-west direction. (A current is very different from a wave. A current consists of a whole mass of water moving steadily along.)

Now if all the tide-producing forces are in simply the east or west direction, you might think that removing the canal walls would have no effect. This is not true, as we shall see. (Furthermore, the forces do in general have north-south components.)

What we must face is the fact that a fluid moving in any direction over the surface of a rotating globe is subject to accelerations and therefore forces which make it deviate from its straight path. Geophysicists call these phenomena *geostrophic effects*. They will modify the motion of any tidal current, and indeed of any tidal wave, since as a wave progresses the water particles have horizontal components of velocity.

In Figure 31a we see the earth in cross section. The line of length r_1 is perpendicular to the earth's axis and intersects the surface of the earth at point P_1. As the earth makes one revolution on its axis, the point P_1 traces out a circle of circumference $2\pi r_1$. Farther south, the point P_2 travels the larger distance $2\pi P_2$ in the same time. The earth's rotation is from west to east, so the velocity v_2 of P_2 to the east is greater than the velocity v_1 of P_1 (Figure 31b). Stand anywhere in the Northern Hemisphere and look south. *Every object that you see is going faster to the east than you are.* Objects to the north of you are going more slowly. This is no trick, no artificiality of language. It is a simple matter of geometry.

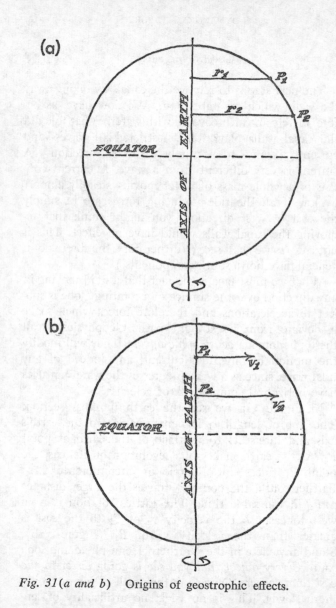

Fig. 31(a and b) Origins of geostrophic effects.

Think, then, of a train heading south. The track ahead of the train always has an eastward velocity greater than that of the train. If the train is to stay on the track it must continually be undergoing an acceleration to the east. Newton, in his second law of motion, says that no acceleration occurs without the application of a net force in the direction of the acceleration. So as long as the train moves south, the tracks are pushing on it with a sidewise force to the east. A physicist usually calls this effect the Coriolis force or Coriolis acceleration, though here Coriolis gets some recognition he doesn't deserve. The matter was understood long before his time!

By similar reasoning, when the train moves north it undergoes a sidewise push to the west. It must *slow down* its eastward velocity. The effect is interesting in the case of a river flowing north or south. Figure 32 represents the bed of a river in cross section. The dotted line is level. For southward flow, the water must be accelerated to the east. Because of inertia the

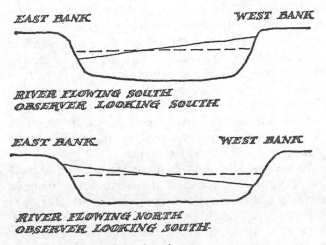

Fig. 32 Cross-section of a river.

water "tilts up" against the west bank. The solid line shows the resulting water surface, though the angle of tilt is much exaggerated. The author, as a physics graduate student, was once given the problem of calculating how much higher the Mississippi River stands on the west bank than on the east bank. The result was not impressive—much less than an inch. Nevertheless, this apparently small effect combined with friction on the river bottom causes the water in a river to flow in a somewhat corkscrew fashion. The result has important effects on river-bank erosion.

The second part of the diagram represents a river flowing north. The tilt is in the opposite direction.

So far we have been talking about objects—the train, the river—caused to move in a constrained path. Think now of a shell fired southward by a cannon. While it is in the air, the shell maintains the eastward component of velocity which it had when it was in the gun. Meanwhile, it is passing over regions of the earth's surface which have increasing velocity to the east. The result: the shell *lands to the west* of the point toward which it was aimed! It is more useful for our purposes to think of a water current moving southward. By the foregoing reasoning, we see that it will be deflected to the right—i.e., to the west. A northward-flowing current will be deflected to the east. It is furthermore true, though not as easy to explain, that Coriolis effects exist for objects moving in *any* direction on the earth's surface—not just north or south. If you visualize motions well in three dimensions, perhaps you will see why this is so.

In any case, the result is that water moving or oscillating north or south must at the same time move or oscillate east or west—and vice versa. If we take away the canal partitions, inevitably there will be circular currents of a complicated nature. The circular motions are one of the most basic aspects of the tides, an aspect which the canal theory denies. We must regretfully discard the canal theory; but don't forget, we obtained from it some important insights.

Attempts to set up dynamical theories

Laplace attempted to create a dynamical theory of the tides. He considered the tides as waves, and set up three complicated partial differential equations for fluid motion, based on the known tidal forces. The equations took into account geostrophic effects. No one has yet been able to solve these equations in their most general form. Laplace used certain simplifications —for example, a homogeneous ocean covering the whole earth—and succeeded after great mathematical labor in obtaining solutions to the equations.

The results are not very helpful, as might be expected. How could they be? There is not *an* ocean, but oceans of the most complicated shapes. Tidal waves cannot travel far without being interrupted by land. Meanwhile they have been passing over ocean bottoms of greatly varying depth. Free waves will also appear, as a result of the natural oscillatory periods of various ocean basins. How incorporate these into a general dynamical theory?

The answer is that it can't be done. Well, then, what is the state of affairs? Are people no longer interested in tidal theory? The answer: many people are interested in explaining the tides, and much progress has been achieved over the years. Progress has been made, however, by practicing "the art of the possible." (That last phrase has been used as a definition of *politics*.) Work has taken two forms: (1) attempts to explain the tides mathematically in idealized ocean basins— round, or rectangular, or consisting of areas bounded by parallels of latitude, or areas between two meridians; (2) attempts to work from tidal observations, using experimental data to produce what might be called a semi-empirical theory.

The second category has been the more successful. There are two objections to the first: to try to explain tides in basins of even the greatest geometrical simplicity leads to enormous mathematical difficulties; the development of modern high-speed computers has helped somewhat, however. An equally telling objection: the actual oceans of the world are extremely complicated in shape. We cannot extrapolate the results for simple basins to actual oceans. We can get, however, some physical insight into actual oceans from looking at the solutions to our idealized equations.

As we shall see in a later chapter, the semi-empirical approach leads to much interesting and useful information. And in localized areas such as bays and estuaries of simple shape, we shall even be able to explain the observed tides on a purely theoretical basis. For this purpose we shall use many of the concepts about waves and periodic motion developed earlier in this chapter.

Chapter V

MEASURING AND PREDICTING
THE TIDES

Measurement of tidal range

As the hours go by, how does the tidal level vary at a given place? What is the maximum rise and fall? These are facts easy to determine, you might say. Surely the measurements are simple and straightforward. But when you stop to think about actual procedures you see some complications.

First, with respect to what arbitrary reference level do you state the height of the water? It would be nice if we could refer all measurements to an *ideal sea level*, a sea surface which is everywhere perpendicular to a plumb line—i.e., to the direction of the earth's gravity at that point. Ideal sea level can exist only as an abstract definition, however. The ocean yields to various forces—astronomical gravitational influences, prevailing winds, the varying density of water masses. What is mean sea level in one region is not that in another. Sea level on the Pacific Coast is higher than that on the Atlantic. The difference is perhaps related to the lower average density of Pacific water.

To be practical, then, we refer our tidal height to some local plane. The plane is often taken to be that of *mean low water*, and this is indeed the reference level for depths as displayed on navigation charts for coastal areas of the United States. Some countries, however, use the average of the height of low-water spring tide, or *mean low-water springs*. Other definitions are also in use. All are equally arbitrary.

How about other complications? If you stop to think of actual experimental methods for measurements of tidal height, you must have anticipated certain difficulties. To drive a "tidal staff"—a pole marked off as a yardstick—into shoal bottom offshore is hardly the answer. The ocean is a restless thing; even in utter calm it stirs and surges. With wind comes another motion, to add to that of the swell.

The problem is evident: to "damp out" the short-period variations in level due to waves. Then the measuring apparatus will respond only to the slow tidal change. One way to do this: dig a well above high-water mark. Drive one end of a horizontal pipe into the well near its bottom, and lead the other end of the pipe down the beach and far enough into the water that it reaches below the lowest tide mark (see Figure 33). Then, since a liquid seeks its own level, the height of the water in the well is that of the ocean. The necessary damping? Easy. Put a constriction in the pipe (an ordinary valve, almost shut, will do nicely) so that water can flow in and out of the well only slowly. The level in the well then cannot follow the short-period variations due to swells and surges. There is plenty of time, however, for the well to adjust to the slow coming or going of the tide.

To record the level in the well as time goes on, make a float, part of whose weight is supported by a vertical wire. The wire winds around a pulley. As the water rises and falls, the pulley turns and moves a pen back and forth across a paper-covered roller driven by clockwork. Thus, automatically, we get a continuous written record of the tide.

We are talking of a method standard for many years.

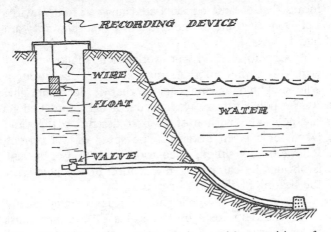

Fig. 33 Measuring tidal change with provision for "damping out" short period variations due to waves.

But recently there have been developed extremely responsive pressure-sensitive devices using solid-state electronics. With great accuracy, these devices convert the pressure they experience into an electric current or potential difference which can then be amplified and recorded automatically. Damping is necessary, as before, but it can be done electrically, by building circuits which respond only to slow changes in the input signal. No more well digging! The pressure transducers can be dropped to the bottom or suspended at any depth by buoys. The wire is led ashore or aboard a survey ship. An even more elegant version contains the recording apparatus within the device itself, which can later be raised and read.

Measurement of tidal currents

Accurate recording of tidal currents is hard, much more difficult in general than measuring tidal heights. The problems increase with depth of water, which means that oceanic currents are the worst to deal with. Let's look at some of the difficulties, and how they are met.

A very old method, one workable in shallow coastal waters, is to anchor the survey ship and throw out a pole weighted at one end so that it floats upright. As the pole drifts away, feed out a light cord tied to the pole, and with a stopwatch determine the time taken for a given distance. The speed of the current follows from a simple calculation. Direction of current is obvious by comparing the motion of the pole with the bearing of the ship's compass.

The method is inefficient and inaccurate—chiefly inefficient. Hundreds or thousands of readings must be taken in a given area to get a clear picture of tidal motion at various points and at various times. Furthermore, by this method you learn only of surface currents—and knowledge of currents at various depths is also very important.

More modern procedures rely on current meters. Such devices come in various forms. Some measure the "ram pressure" of the current on a plate or Pitot tube. Others—the more common type—are shaped like small torpedoes, and like torpedoes have a propeller at the end. A rudder keeps them pointing into the current. The device is fixed in place, usually by attachment to a moored cable. Current speed may then be measured—in one version of the apparatus—in terms of the torque produced on the propeller, which is not allowed to rotate. In another version, the propeller does rotate as the current streams by, and its rate of revolution is recorded.

The *direction* of flow is determined by a magnetic compass or gyro compass mounted within the instrument, and connected to the recording apparatus. (Direction, by the way, is always given as that *toward which the current flows.*)

Typically, several such meters are fastened to a cable at various depths. The cable is anchored at the bottom. Lift is provided by a buoy. In apparatus now being used by the United States Coast and Geodetic Survey, the buoy is boat-shaped with a length of ten feet and a beam of five feet. A mast holds a radar reflector, so that the buoy can easily be found even in conditions of poor visibility. A 1500-watt flashing light warns shipping. Atop the mast is a radio antenna. Radio range is some 20 to 30 miles (see Plate 2).

These meters are attended by a survey ship which collects the data. On receipt of a coded radio command from the ship, a given meter will broadcast its data via the transmitter on the buoy. The information is recorded on tape in the ship's radio room. Each buoy is queried regularly and in turn. A buoy is seldom left in one spot for more than a week or two.

At the time this book is written, the Coast and Geodetic Survey is near the end of a three-year study of the currents near Block Island and in Long Island Sound.

In deep water, measurements require different techniques. Anchoring of a ship or buoy, even if possible, is usually unsatisfactory. At the end of such a long line the swing due to winds and currents is apt to be great. It is enough, in fact, to prevent accurate determination of the small current velocities characteristic of the open ocean.

Instead, drift buoys are often used. The buoy may have a radio transmitter, so that its progress can be tracked by direction finders on ship and on shore. Or its motion may be followed by a radar-equipped vessel. To get information about currents at various depths, one can use a parachute drogue. The drogue is attached at the depth desired. Since currents at differing depths may flow in various directions, the buoy is sometimes seen "steaming along" at an angle to or even straight against the surface current, as if the device contained its own engine!

Another, more sophisticated, device is the neutrally buoyant float which can be set to hover freely at any depth. The float contains a sonar transmitter which emits signals at regular intervals. An accompanying ship tracks the device by means of its hydrophones.

Determination of currents by following a drift buoy obviously requires knowledge of the position of the ship itself. Fortunately, modern electronic aids to navigation such as loran give this knowledge, though not always as accurately as one might wish.

Harmonic analysis of the tides

You will remember, from Chapter III, the myriad of periodicities associated with the tidal forces. These periodicities arise from the complicated motions, with respect to the earth, of the sun and moon. Each period can be identified with some aspect of astronomical behavior; the tide associated with it is called a *partial tide*, or *harmonic* of the tide.

Another way of stating the idea: the observed tide in any region is the sum of a number of partial tides. The partial tides are simple harmonic oscillations of various periods. Each period corresponds to the cycle of some aspect of the astronomical tide-generating forces.

Contained in the above statements is the entire concept of harmonic analysis of the tides and its use for predicting tidal behavior. To understand the matter fully we must see exactly what we mean by a partial tide. At this point, we can do no better than to follow the argument developed by George Darwin (son of Charles Darwin, author of *Origin of Species*). Darwin's book entitled *The Tides* was published in 1898.

To begin, let's simplify matters by assuming that

only one other celestial object exists—the moon. Furthermore, the moon is revolving in a circle in the earth's equatorial plane. Then each tide is exactly the same for all time. Successive crests occur every 12 hours and 25 minutes.

Now this is not to say that high water occurs when the moon is overhead. We've seen the complexities which prevent such a synchronization. But *for a given locality* the time of high water due to a given partial tide will occur a definite and unchanging number of hours before or after the passage of the moon. Also, the amount of rise and fall will always be the same. The tide, in other words, could be predicted for all time in terms of two constants: the amount of rise and fall, and the interval between the moon's passage and high water.

Suppose we replace the moon by the sun, also revolving in a circle about the earth's equator, but at the sun's present distance from the earth. The time between crests now changes to exactly twelve hours. Two new constants appear, expressing, as before, the tidal interval and height.

Now, keeping the sun, bring back the moon in its equatorial circle. The two tidal waves combine, in a way which can be predicted by use of the four available constants. How? Given the future moment at which we wish to know the tide, we look in a table of astronomical data to find the time elapsed since the sun and the moon crossed the meridian. We then calculate the height of each tide alone with the help of its two characteristic constants. By adding the results we get the actual tide.

But our picture so far is absurdly simplified. The sun and moon actually move in planes tipped so that these celestial objects are sometimes to the north, sometimes to the south, of the equator. Furthermore, the eccentricity of their orbits means that their distances from the earth, and therefore their tidal influences, are constantly changing.

The effect of these conditions can be dealt with by a mathematical artifice, in which many fictitious "moons" and "suns" are introduced. These objects are of various masses and move in various planes. They need not obey dynamical laws—that is, they need not be such that if a *real* object were there, it would have to follow the given path. Rather, we assign their orbits arbitrarily. Some, in fact, have no orbits. They stand still among the stars. Others move backward.

What is the sense of all this, which seems an incomprehensible complication of the state of affairs? Simply the following: the artificial masses and orbits are so chosen that the sum of their tidal forces corresponds exactly to those of an actual sun and moon as they move in their real paths. Each fictitious object stands still or moves in a simple orbit. It creates, therefore, a tide of simple harmonic character. This tide repeats itself predictably with a certain periodicity; it is known for all time.

In principle, then, knowledge of the two constants describing each of the simple harmonic, or partial, tides would allow us to combine these tides to describe the actual tide, and predict its behavior at any time. Getting the constants, however, is quite an operation. Their value depends on the place of observation. We must record the actual tide at this place over a great length of time—perhaps twenty years. Variations of long period will then be included, and random changes (due, for example, to meteorological effects) will average out.

Given the actual tidal data, what do we do? We apply the method of *harmonic analysis*, a mathematical technique in which a function, in this case a quantitative expression for the actual tidal wave, is separated into its harmonic constituents. The more partial tides there are, the more difficult the process. Believe it or not, the complete list of measurably significant partial tides numbers around 390! To untangle them would be a task of gargantuan proportions. Fortunately only some twelve are large enough to be worth consideration. In practice, for moderate accuracy, we can often work with seven—four components of approximately semi-diurnal periodicity, and three of approximately diurnal.

Offhand, you might think that with this limitation we neglect the very important fortnightly variations. Not so. As we add the tidal constants for each of these seven tides with their different periodicities, we automatically come up with the longer-period behavior. For example, the time difference between successive solar tides is about twenty-five minutes shorter than that between successive lunar tides. Thus the difference amounts to some fifty minutes a day. If at a certain time the two high waters happen to be simultaneous, then about seven days later the solar tide will be approximately six hours ahead of the lunar. The high water of one will be the low water of the other. Seven more days, and they are in phase again. Thus we get the phenomenon of spring and neap tides.

As another example, how do we account for the periodicity associated with the elliptic orbit of the moon? Easily, by postulating a "lunar elliptic" partial tide of period 12 hours, 39 minutes, and 30 seconds. The period of the principal lunar tide, stated with equal accuracy, is 12 hours, 25 minutes, and 14 seconds. Thus the principal lunar tide gains on the lunar elliptic tide by 28 minutes and 32 seconds each day. If the two start in synchronism they will be out of phase some thirteen days later—as a matter of fact, after just one-half of an anomalistic month has passed. The anomalistic month, you will recall, is the time for the moon to go from perigee to perigee. Thus by suitably choosing the amplitude of the lunar elliptic partial tide we account for the tidal variations due to the changing earth-moon distance.

By now you see the rationale. We account for all the complexities of astronomical behavior by choosing suitable "harmonics." To summarize, then: we consider the actual tide at any place to be the sum of a number of partial tides. Each of the latter repeats itself at a constant rate, and the amount of its rise and fall is constant. Thus, if we can determine the pair of constants characteristic of each partial tide we can predict the actual tide. The more partial tides we include the better the accuracy. We take only enough to provide useful prediction of tidal behavior.

Your next question is inevitable. Given the actual tidal record in a certain region, how does one go about deducing the partial tides? How, in other words, do you find quantitatively what part of the total tide is due to a particular harmonic? The task at first seems hopeless.

What do we have to go on? One thing—we know the periodicity of each partial tide. It appears regularly at this interval. Then why not mark off time on our tidal record in units of this particular "day"? If we take a long-term average of rise and fall on the basis of this one time scale, all variations due to partial tides of other periods will vanish. They "average out" of existence. What is left is the tide we're looking for. All that remains is to repeat the process for each of the partial tides we want to include.

"All that remains . . ." The prospect of the calculational procedure is horrendous—in human terms, that is. Before the days of high-speed computers it was done, but only at great labor and through the use of some clever approximation methods. Now we can program a computer to do the averaging and searching—a procedure which still means enormous amounts of data-processing and computing. But then, no one takes pity on an electronic computer.

Prediction of the tides

We found that, given two constants which characterize each partial tide, we can synthesize the actual tide as the sum of these components. What we need is a machine—mechanical or electrical—to do the process automatically.

In principle the problem is elementary. Each partial tide is, after all, a simple harmonic function of the time. The plot is merely a sine or a cosine curve. One of the two constants for the particular tide gives the amplitude of the curve, and the other its phase. We need a means of summing these curves.

Let's speak first in mechanical terms. Figure 34 shows

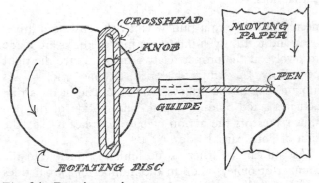

Fig. 34 Drawing a sine curve.

a device for drawing a sine curve. A disk with a projecting knob rotates at a uniform, suitably chosen speed. The knob projects into a slot in a crosshead. As the disk rotates, the crosshead is drawn back and forth with simple harmonic motion. An extension arm fastened to the crosshead holds a pen. Beneath the pen is a strip of paper, moved forward at constant speed by some mechanism. The result: a sine curve drawn on the paper, a curve which could represent a partial tide. The amplitude can be controlled by how far from the center of the disk the knob is placed.

But how to add two such motions? Look at Figure 35. Here are two disks and two crossheads, each con-

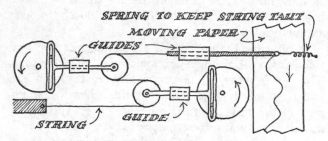

Fig. 35   Drawing a curve that represents the sum of two partial tides.

nected this time to a pulley which the crosshead drives back and forth. By suitable gearing, the disks are made to revolve at the proper relative speed to give the right periodicity. A string, fastened at one end, passes around each of the pulleys. The other end of the string actuates a rod holding a pen. The motion of the pen thus represents the action of both crossheads—i.e., the sum of both partial tides.

As you can see, there is no limit in principle to the number of pulleys—i.e., to the number of partial tides which can be inserted. Just be sure that the string loops around each pulley. Also be sure that the knob on each disk is placed radially to give the proper amplitude, and that when the machine is started each knob has the right angular position to provide the proper phase. In this way the two constants for each harmonic are inserted into the machine.

This, in effect, is the mode of operation of any of the

many successful tide-predicting machines now in existence. To be sure, as the number of partial tides to be
accounted for increases, the gearing becomes very complicated. Accuracy of the result requires high crafts-
manship in the fabrication of the machine.

Until a few years ago all tide-predicting machines
were mechanical. Now we have electronic computers
to do the job much more quickly and efficiently.
It is possible to create, in mathematical analogue, the
simple harmonic motions of the mechanical machines,
and sum them. The computers can be programmed to
print out the tide tables automatically. Starting with the
year 1966, all high- and low-water predictions of the
United States Coast and Geodetic Survey are made
in this fashion. Four volumes are issued annually. They
are: Europe, the Mediterranean, and West Coast of
Africa; East Coast, North and South America; West
Coast, North and South America; Pacific and Indian
Oceans. Full daily forecasts are made for 196 reference
stations. The reader can obtain information for about
six thousand subordinate stations, however, by using
the "Tables of Tidal Differences" included in each
volume.

Improved methods of prediction are under study.
One method recognizes the fact that the partial tides
are, after all, not completely independent of one another. There are "non-linear interactions" in any given
location. To a certain extent these interactions can be
formulated and incorporated in the computer program.
The result is a better prediction.

How accurate are tidal predictions? If the weather
is calm and the barometer steady they are surely good
enough for any practical purpose. *But*—a wind toward
the land raises the water level; an area of high barometric pressure lowers it. No tide table can foretell
such effects. The prudent navigator will allow for a
reasonable margin of error.

Chapter VI

TIDES AND TIDAL CURRENTS IN SMALL AREAS

We have seen the how and why of the ocean tides—how gravitational tide-generating forces exist, and why they cause the waters of the earth to rise and fall. And we have seen something of how people measure tidal heights and tidal currents, and analyze the data for the prediction of tidal behavior.

What we haven't talked about is tides on the local scene—tides as they appear to the clam digger at his backbreaking task, or to the sailor in a dungeon of fog, hearing the crash of breakers and wondering if the course that he has laid out to the next bell buoy allowed correctly for the "set of the tide." And even the dweller on the shore of a large lake sees something of the tide, though he seldom recognizes it as such. We can hardly blame him, for on lakes the effect of the tide-generating forces is small and often obscured, as we shall see, by a much greater rise and fall due to other phenomena.

Tides in lakes

Small as the tidal effect on lakes may be, we had better talk of it first. Lakes are the simplest bodies of water to examine. We have seen the horrible complications of ocean tides. Geostrophic effects, friction, shore configurations, and other factors all make the understanding of ocean tidal behavior a chancy thing. But on lakes many of these complicating factors are missing. Geostrophic forces can ordinarily be neglected because of the small area involved, and for the same reason so can certain other effects. Furthermore, in lakes—at least, in those of a fairly regular shape and depth—one can come to understand the system of standing and progressive waves that is observed. This system is generated only in small part by the tidal forces. Winds and changing barometric pressure are more efficient.

But the point is this, and it is an important one: we can see what sort of "tidal" waves, what sort of "sloshing back and forth," is possible in a given enclosed body of water, whatever the cause. Then we can apply our resulting knowledge to ocean gulfs, bays, river estuaries—where tides enormous in comparison with those of lakes exist and must be understood.

Putting the matter in another way: a body of salt water in communication with the ocean will have a system of progressive and standing waves basically similar to that of a lake of like configuration. The difference lies in the fact that one part of the bay is open to the ocean. Thus the rise and fall of the ocean tide will feed energy into the enclosure with a certain periodicity. In words of the mathematical physicist, we have, in the case of a lake, a freely vibrating system (once some disturbance has displaced the surface from equilibrium). In a bay, we have a system capable of free vibrations but subject to externally applied periodic forces. We call the resulting situation that of forced oscillations. These oscillations are usually of much larger amplitude than those of the unforced systems, because energy is continually fed in to make up for that lost in frictional effects.

It is no exaggeration to say that the tide, wherever observed, comes about in a complicated interplay of free and forced vibrations, whose character is determined by local conditions. In most cases the shape of the bay or gulf or river estuary is so complicated, and the water depth so various, that exact mathematical solution is impossible. Only for the simplest situations can an approximate prediction be made on the basis of the theory of oscillations. Usually, people approach the problem in another way: they make careful observations of tidal heights and currents as the hours go by. Then, essentially by trial and error, they see what system of forced oscillations can be invented to explain what is happening.

Inevitably, resonances play a large role. A system ordinarily has several different natural periods of vibration. If one or more of these periods is close to the period of the tide, or to an integral multiple or submultiple of it, reinforcement will occur. Tidal range within the bay may be, and usually is, much greater than that in the ocean immediately outside.

The range of tides in the open ocean is, indeed, pretty unexciting—perhaps two or three feet. What we describe as "good big tides" *must* arise as local phenomena involving some sort of resonance. Later we will look at actual examples.

But first, what of lakes—big lakes? They have to be big if, in them, tides of astronomical origin are to be seen. Such tides are, in fact, seldom observed in the direct sense. Changes in water level there are, and sometimes fairly large, but the behavior—as recorded, perhaps, on a sensitive tide gauge—seems random. This is not surprising. As we have already said, rise and fall due to varying winds and barometric pressure overshadow the effects of the tidal forces. Can we deduce the actual tides in large lakes? Yes, by searching in the data for a component which varies with tidal periodicity. A suitably programmed computer can do this and come up with a reasonably accurate value of the tidal range.

It will be interesting to see how these observed tidal variations can be linked to some of the simple ideas about waves which we discussed in Chapter IV. Think of a channel running parallel to the lines of latitude, that is, in an east-west direction. The channel is of constant depth and sealed at both ends, so that it forms a narrow rectangular basin. Suppose some force causes the water to rise at one end of the basin. When the force is removed, a mass movement of water will take place toward the other end of the basin. Because of inertia, this movement will not stop when the surface of the channel is level. The water will overshoot

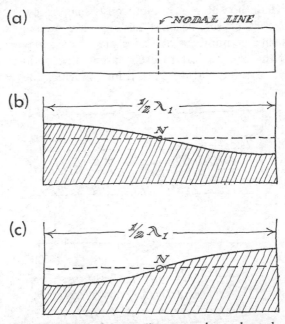

Fig. 36 A mononodal standing wave in a channel running east-west in a sealed basin.

and pile up at the other end; then the process will be reversed. In this way an oscillation is set up about a fixed axis which is halfway down the channel. The fixed axis, which extends across the channel, is a nodal line. Part (a) in Figure 36 shows a top view of the basin. In (b) we have a side view when the water is heaped up at the west end and in (c) when the water has risen at the east end. We have the condition of a standing wave, of wavelength λ_1. Other standing waves are possible, of course. The only "boundary condition" is that the ends of the channel be anti-nodes. Here the water can have only vertical motion. Thus the mononodal wave of Figure 36 could be replaced by or superimposed upon a binodal standing wave of wavelength λ_2 ($\frac{1}{2}$ λ_1) as shown in Figure 37. Here the water is simultaneously high or low at the two ends of the basin. Standing wave systems with still greater numbers of nodes are obviously possible.

If the basin is left to itself except for a sudden impulse of some sort to start things moving, the water

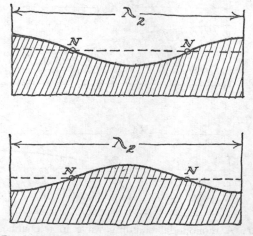

Fig. 37 A binodal standing wave.

sloshes freely back and forth. (Eventually, of course, the oscillation dies out because of frictional effects.) The characteristic period of sloshing depends upon the length and depth of the channel, and upon which of the various modes of oscillation has been put into being. We have described above the two simplest modes. The higher the mode, i.e., the more nodal lines, the shorter the characteristic period.

What of actual astronomical tides in large lakes? It is interesting to see how big they are, and on what their amplitude depends. Consider the effect of the continuously applied tide-generating force. (For simplicity, we shall speak of this force as if it had only one component, the lunar semi-diurnal.) This force, we suppose, is the only one disturbing the water of the basin, and the standing waves produced must therefore have a period equal to that of the tidal force. It is a case of forced, not free, oscillation.

Now recall another idea developed in Chapter IV, where we spoke of canals encircling the earth. If the period of the free wave is smaller than that of the tide-generating force, the motion follows that force and we have equilibrium tides. If the free period is larger, the motion is out of phase. Low water appears when the tide-generating force is greatest and vice versa. When one of the characteristic periods of oscillation happens to coincide with that of the tidal forces, resonance will occur for that particular mode, and larger tidal effects may be expected.

If a canal or channel is closed at its end so that it does not encircle the earth, the situation is somewhat different. We no longer have a tidal rise which is exactly in phase or exactly out of phase with the tidal force. Mathematically speaking, the boundary conditions describing the fact that the basin *does* have closed ends must be added to the equations of motion. The result: changes in the phase relations.

Obviously, whatever happens in a lake must depend a great deal on its characteristic periods of oscillation.

Suppose, by harmonic analysis, we separate out from our data the actual tides in a large enclosed body of water. Can we explain them on the basis of theory? Certainly their nature will depend on many factors, and so far we have greatly oversimplified the problem. The usual lake does not even approximate a rectangular basin. Its width varies, as does its depth. Unless the lake is extremely narrow, transverse oscillations can occur in addition to the longitudinal ones we have been considering. The whole matter requires lengthy mathematical treatment. But for certain lakes such calculations have been done. What are the results, and how do they compare with observations?

Let's take as our first example studies done on Lake Erie. Here, at the west end, the observed semi-diurnal tidal amplitude is 5.2 centimeters, compared to a computed value of 5.4 centimeters. The good agreement is proof that we are observing actual astronomical tides. What about the *time* of high water? In a lake it is not profitable to imagine, as we did earlier for the ocean, a traveling bulge of water. Instead, we recall that the horizontal component (which is all that counts) of the tide-generating force reaches its maximum at points on the earth's surface which are located about 45 degrees from the zenith. Thus if we have a clock which reads noon when the moon passes our zenith, the greatest force to the west will come at 3 P.M. The greatest force to the east occurs at 9 A.M.

For a sufficiently small lake, where the characteristic period is less than that of the tidal force, we should expect the tide to be in phase with that force—a direct tide. High water at the west end of the lake should then occur at about three hours lunar time, and at the east end, at nine hours. But for Lake Erie, the opposite is true: high tide at Buffalo comes about three, and at Amherstburg on the west end about nine. Theory therefore predicts that the mononodal period of free oscillation for Lake Erie is greater than twelve hours; observation shows that this is indeed true. For Lake Balaton in Hungary, on the other hand, where the characteristic period has been measured as about nine and one-half hours, the western end has high tide at three hours.

We should mention one more matter. In our general discussion of standing waves we have spoken of water as sloshing back and forth, rising and falling at a given location. But we have not made clear the relation between *currents* and *elevations*. For simplicity, let us think of a mononodal oscillation in a rectangular basin. Across the central part of the basin is a nodal line along which there is no rise and fall of the lake's surface. Suppose the situation at the moment is that of Figure 38a. The water has attained its maximum height at one end and matters are static. No part of the water mass is moving. The situation is unstable, however. There is obviously a tendency for water to flow back to the west. Let the period of a complete (from one end to the other and back again) oscillation be called T. At the moment shown in Part (a) set the elapsed time t equal to o. At $t = o$, then, the water is at rest, but there is a force tending to create an acceleration to the left and a current therefore begins. At time $t = \dfrac{T}{4}$ Part (b), the surface is level and the currents have their maximum values to the left. The lengths of the arrows are proportional to the swiftness of the currents. Note an interesting thing: the *elevation node* N is a *current anti-node*. Here the currents are fastest, not just at this particular time in the cycle, but always. For example, in Part (c) the water is approaching its highest level at the west end. Currents still exist but they are smaller.

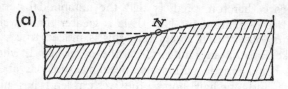

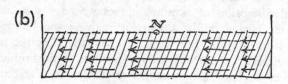

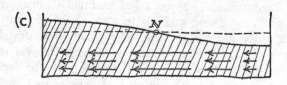

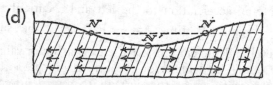

Fig. 38 Currents in a mononodal oscillation (a,b,c) and a binodal oscillation (d), with maximum currents appearing at the elevation nodes N.

Their largest speed, however, is still at N. At $t = \frac{T}{2}$ the situation becomes static again. Then the motion is reversed. The surface is level at $t = \frac{3}{4}T$, but all currents are to the right. At $t = T$ we regain the situation of $t = 0$. The same arguments apply to more complicated oscillations, where the number of elevation nodes is greater than one. Part (d) shows the currents in a binodal oscillation as the water is nearing maximum heights at both ends of the basin. Here, as before, maximum currents appear at the elevation nodes N. But there is a *current nodal line* at N'. Along this line the water never moves, even though it is an antinode so far as elevation is concerned. We can say that elevation and current are completely out of phase with each other.

Soon we shall see, in our study of tides in basins open to the ocean, how important the phase relations between elevation and current are.

Tides in bays and gulfs

Tides—real tides—in lakes are hardly awesome in magnitude, as we have just seen. Their height, even in large lakes, is of the order of inches. (A big wind on such a lake, however, can cause changes in level of several feet.) If tidal effects on lakes are so small, why can we have, in similar-size basins open to the ocean, tides which are enormous in comparison? To explain this is our task of the moment.

At the start, to make things easier, we will assume a bay of rectangular shape and constant depth. It is very small (so that we can forget about *its own* tides), longer than it is wide, and one end is completely open to the ocean. The tide-producing force is parallel to the long axis of the bay.

Now so far, in our discussion of free oscillations, we

have been speaking of them as occurring in a basin *both ends of which are closed.* Standing waves were formed. The contents of the basin could slosh back and forth like water in a bathtub. Can the same sort of thing occur when one end of the basin is open? Surprisingly, the answer is yes, although it is harder to see why. We shall not go through the mathematical proof. Instead, remember that a whistle usually consists of a tube with one end open. When you blow it you set up standing waves—free oscillations of the air column—inside. Waves can be and are reflected from the open end. As another example: organ pipes come in two varieties—both ends closed or one end open and one end closed. Both open and closed ends, then, can cause reflection and the formation of a standing wave.

Our open bay behaves in the same way. It has characteristic periods of free oscillation. But it communicates directly with the ocean, which is rising and falling under the influence of the tidal forces. At the mouth of the bay the water must obviously always correspond in height to that of the ocean. The bay is therefore forced into *co-oscillation* with the ocean. Energy is fed from the ocean into the basin to form a system of standing waves, or a co-oscillating tide. The nature of this system, as we have seen, will depend on the relation between the characteristic periods of free oscillation and the period of the tidal rise and fall outside.

Let's assume for the present that friction is negligible. If we set up equations for a co-oscillating tide of the type we are considering, we can predict the behavior of the basin, given its length and depth. Let R be the ratio between the periods of the free and the tidal oscillations. Figure 39 shows the shape of the surface at a time when the water at the open end has a certain elevation above mean sea level. The diagrams correspond to various values of R, as indicated.

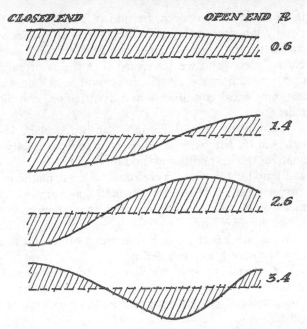

Fig. 39 A bay in co-oscillation with the ocean.

Resonance occurs, the equations predict, for $R = 1$, 3, 5, 7, ... Mathematically speaking, in the absence of frictional effects the amplitude at resonance becomes infinite. This is physically meaningless, of course. Friction is always present to prevent enormous amplitudes. Nevertheless, the effects in an actual bay when R is close to a resonance value are often very striking. Soon we will look at some actual examples of such effects.

It is useful to think of the co-oscillating tide as the superposition of an incoming tidal wave on the wave completely reflected from the closed end. If reflection at the closed end is perfect—i.e., no energy is lost—we have the necessary condition for a standing wave. In a real bay, of course, reflection can't be perfect. Even

76405

if the basin itself is deep, friction is introduced by the rapidly shoaling water at the upper end. So the actual situation only approximates that of a standing wave. Nevertheless (and we have seen that this is often the case) we can make certain important conclusions by assuming ideal conditions—in this situation, complete reflection.

What about actual basins? Can we explain their behavior on the basis of theory? As soon as we try to analyze the co-oscillating tide in a bay of irregular width and varying depth we run into great mathematical complexities. If the bay is small, however, there are methods of numerical integration that allow a fairly good approximation to the observed tide. These methods are based on our knowledge of the idealized bays we have been considering.

For several reasons we have restricted discussion so far to small bodies of water. Let us look at some of the complications which appear in the larger bays and gulfs.

The first fact that we must face: the tide-generating force is not always in an east-west direction. If you look again at Figure 9, you will see that to an observer being carried around a circle of latitude on a rotating earth, the tidal force is continually varying in direction as well as magnitude. Only when the observer is on the equator and the moon is in the plane of the equator does the tide-generating force have a purely east-west component. In general there is a north-south component too. In each of the diagrams in Figure 40 the arrow represents the semi-diurnal tidal force at different times of lunar day. The direction of the force is referred to north-south and east-west axes, and the magnitude is proportional to the length of the arrow. As time goes on, the tip of the arrow traces out an elliptical path. Time is indicated by the numerals around the outside of the ellipse. Diagrams are

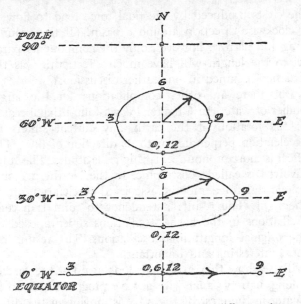

Fig. 40 The semi-diurnal tidal force at different times of the lunar day.

shown for an observer in the Northern Hemisphere at latitudes 0°, 30°, 60°, and 90°. The moon is assumed to be in the plane of the earth's equator. The tidal force at the poles (latitude 90°) is therefore zero.

At the equator, the tidal force alternates on an east-west line. It is maximum to the east at 9 o'clock and to the west at 3 o'clock. It is zero at 6 and 12. For latitudes between 0° and 90°, there is a component to the south from 0 to 3 o'clock and from 9 to 12 o'clock. A component exists to the north from 3 to 9 o'clock. These components to the north and south reach their maximums at 6 and 12 respectively.

What is the result of this constantly varying direction? At 9 o'clock the water is pulled to the east, at 12 to the south, at 3 to the west, at 6 to the north. Thus

the crests produced by the tidal force tend to flow in
a clockwise direction around a basin. (If the basin is
long and narrow, however, only the components parallel to the length will have much effect; this was the
situation assumed in our earlier discussion.)

But there are other complications for the larger
bodies of water. In Chapter IV we found that because
of the rotation of the earth, any current suffers an
acceleration perpendicular to its direction of flow. The
effect is more pronounced at higher latitudes. The force
involved is called geostrophic. In the Northern Hemisphere this force and the associated acceleration are to
the right. The result: a tendency to form transverse
oscillations in the basin, oscillations superimposed on
the original longitudinal oscillations. The results are
most interesting and important.

To see how they arise, let's look again at the case of
a long, narrow canal with a wave progressing down it.
Water in the crest of the wave is moving in the direction of progress. Because of the crosswise "heaping up"
of the water due to the geostrophic effect, the wave-
crest slopes downward from right to left. The geostrophic force exactly balances the component of gravity acting down the slope. When a trough arrives the
current is reversed. The water now flows backward and
the direction of crosswise slope is just the opposite. So
we see that a transverse oscillation is produced. Another consequence: since the water slopes downward
to the left from its high position on the right-hand
wall, and downward to the right from its low position
on the left-hand wall, the result is large amplitudes of
the tidal wave on the right-hand side and small amplitudes on the left-hand side.

You may object and say, "Surely these transverse
oscillations must be negligibly small. The earth turns
slowly and the geostrophic acceleration is tiny." True
enough—so far as the last part of the statement is con-

cerned. At a latitude of 45° and with a current of 8 inches per second (reasonable for a tidal wave) the crosswise deviation of the water's surface from the vertical is only 0.4 second of arc. Thus the transverse slope is extraordinarily small. *But* so is the forward-and-aft slope of the tidal wave. This wave may be, say, 120 miles long and only one foot high. The longitudinal slope of this wave is only about two seconds of arc —five times that of the crosswise slope. The two slopes are therefore of the same order of magnitude, and the transverse oscillation is *not* negligible in comparison with the longitudinal one.

A wave of the sort we have been discussing is called a Kelvin wave after Lord Kelvin, who first made an analytical study of the phenomenon. The condition of a long, narrow canal is of course highly artificial. But some of the ideas which come from it can be applied to a body of water of any shape. Longitudinal oscillations are bound to be accompanied by transverse oscillations, and these in turn by transverse motions of the water particles. The combination of transverse and longitudinal oscillations results in a *rotational* motion of the wave particles. We shall talk about this rotation a little later.

Let's ask first how actual tide waves will behave, in the light of the considerations above. If we have a standing wave in the basin due to a co-oscillating tide, the longitudinal currents will be greatest at the nodes, as already explained. The amplitudes of the transverse oscillation will thus be largest here. This means that the tide will be zero *only* at the center point of the original nodal line! No longer do we have a nodal line extending across the bay. If we stand looking into the bay, high water will occur on the right-hand end of the original nodal line one-quarter period before it happens at the closed end of the bay. On the left side it will occur one-quarter period after.

Thus when we have both longitudinal and transverse oscillations, the tide is zero at a single place only, called an *amphidromic point*. It is useful to join all points which have high water or low water at the same time by *cotidal lines*. These lines must necessarily all meet at an amphidromic point. Figure 41, depicting a bay

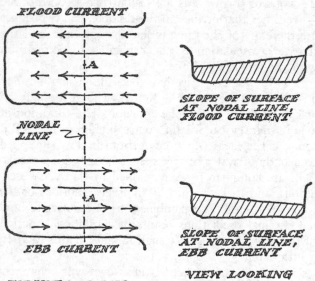

Fig. 41 Transverse and longitudinal oscillations for an incoming and an outgoing tide.

of rectangular shape, will help to make the whole business clearer. The transverse slope of the surface at the original nodal line is shown for both an incoming tide at $t = 0$, and for an outgoing tide at $t = \dfrac{T}{2}$, where T is the period of the tidal oscillation. The amphidromic point is at A.

Figure 42 shows a system of cotidal lines. Since the

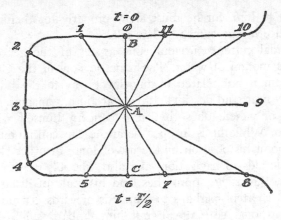

Fig. 42 Cotidal lines connect points having high water at the same time.

transverse oscillations differ from the longitudinal by one-quarter period, we have high water at point B at $t = 0$ and at point C at $t = \frac{T}{2}$. The numbers around the outside are lunar clock hours. We see that the cotidal lines rotate around the amphidromic point in a counterclockwise direction.

Tidal currents

Currents are as much a part of tidal phenomena as the rise and fall of the ocean surface. A mariner would probably say, in fact, that currents are the more important. Only when a vessel is entering or leaving a harbor does the navigator ordinarily worry about water depth.* Currents on the other hand are a constant con-

* Sometimes he has to keep a *very close* check! Recently I was on the bridge of a ferry crossing the estuary of the River Humber in England. Looking astern, I saw to my dismay that the churning wake was a mass of light-brown

cern to him, for he must allow properly for their influence in any course he lays out.

Tidal currents are only one aspect of the general mass motion of water. The majestic flow of the Gulf Stream is not related in any direct way to the tides. Only near land do tidal currents attain any magnitude, and only here does the sailor concern himself with them. While he is in open ocean he can continuously pinpoint his position by the use of loran or other electronic aids to navigation, and also "shoot" the sun or stars. But as he approaches land his scale of distance must shorten—perhaps to hundreds of yards. An unexpected tidal current can put him embarrassingly far away from the harbor mouth. If he has radar and makes a continuous radar plot he can, of course, correct for the set of the tide—once he discovers it exists. But the competent skipper has at hand a book of tables, for example the "Tidal Current Tables" published annually for different areas of the American coast by the U. S. Coast and Geodetic Survey. Here, for the principal harbors and straits, he can find for any day of the year (a) the speeds of the maximum currents in ebb and flood and the times at which they occur, (b) the direction, in degrees true, of ebb and flood, (c) the time of slack water (no current), (d) the means of calculating the speed for any time, given the maximum current and the time interval between maximum current and slack water. He can also find, for offshore areas and wider indentations of the coast, a description of the rotary tidal currents which he may encounter.

What does he do with this sort of information? Let's take a simple numerical example. In Figure 43, the

foam. Diffidently I asked the pilot the depth of the water. "Six feet." And how much did the ship draw? "Five and one-half feet."

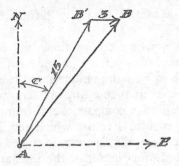

Fig. 43 Calculating a course.

ship is initially at position A. The navigator wishes to go in a straight line to point B. His tables, however, tell him that there is at the moment an easterly set of tide of three knots. The ship's speed through the water is fifteen knots. He knows that his actual velocity with respect to the earth will be the vector sum of the ship's velocity AB' and the current velocity B'B. The sum is the vector AB. So he lays out the distance AB' in a line 15 units long and the distance B'B in a line 3 units long, and joins them in such a way that the vector sum AB lies in the desired direction. He then measures the angle C and has his answer. This is the course which he must steer.

To the skipper of a sailboat, tidal currents are a constant challenge and menace. He is usually poking about in various bays and harbors of the coast, where the currents are often complicated and not well predicted by tables and charts. In the more northern latitudes, fog is always imminent; it can close in with little warning. The wise sailor lays out his corrected course even though the destination is at the moment in plain sight. You can sail for three hours—as has the writer—in apparently clear weather toward distant Monhegan Island off the coast of Maine—and then suddenly and fantastically, in a matter of thirty seconds, the island vanishes!

Or perhaps you are sailing along the coast and a spell of fog has holed you up in some harbor. At last, no longer able to bear the unique smell from the local fish cannery, you up anchor anyway. You will lick the fog. And so you set a compass course from the marker at the harbor mouth, a course which should take you to the whistle buoy off Roaring Bull Ledge. You try to allow correctly for the set of the tide, and for your boat's slight drift to leeward as you sail.

And so you push ahead through the white prison, rising and falling on the heavy silent swell. No sound but the swish of the bow wave and the creak of the gooseneck. Your patent log, which measures distance traveled, is streamed over the stern; by now, it says, you should be hearing the whistle. But you hear nothing. Are you too far offshore? Or has a current carried you inshore and near the deadly embrace of Roaring Bull?

The cry of a gull knifes through the air, and the palms of your hands get a little moist; gulls stay close to land—or ledges. And then at last, faintly, the moan of the buoy, and almost dead ahead. You feel better; you're not such a bad navigator after all. But in your heart you know you were lucky.

How large may tidal currents become? So far as the open ocean is concerned, this is not an easy question to answer. It seems clear that away from land tidal currents cannot reach great velocities. What currents there are usually rotate—clockwise in the Northern Hemisphere. This clockwise tendency supports the view that they are the result of geostrophic effects. Speeds are typically about one knot.

When strong tidal currents occur in narrow sounds, the water is ordinarily busily engaged in filling or emptying a basin. Let's take as an example a certain bay

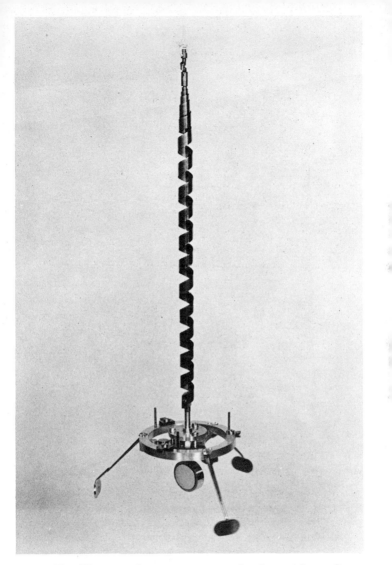

1. The Hoyt gravimeter measures the force of gravity. A change in gravity causes the spring, from which a weight is hung, to extend and rotate; the change can be calculated, then, by measuring the degree of rotation. (Gulf Research and Development Company)

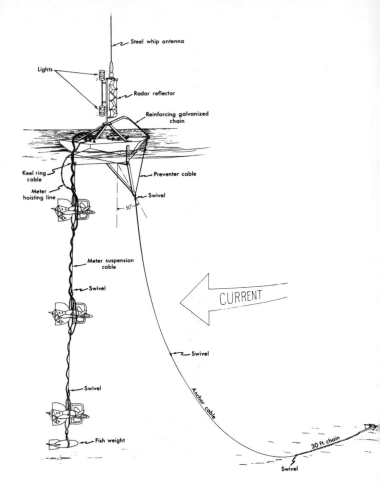

2. Current meters are fastened at various depths to a cable attached to a buoy. A survey ship collects data on tidal currents which is broadcast from the meters via the buoy transmitter. (Coast and Geodetic Survey)

3. The famous tides of the Bay of Fundy, New Brunswick, Canada, are the highest in the world. When they recede, they leave behind broad beaches and helplessly stranded small boats. This scene at Alma is typical of communities along the shore of the bay. (New Brunswick Travel Bureau)

4. The St. John River at low tide surges over the rapids at Reversing Falls. At high tide, the Bay of Fundy tides force their way upstream and the falls run backward. (New Brunswick Travel Bureau)

5. Men work at low tide on fishnets in the Bay of Fundy. Pieces of seaweed caught in the fine mesh near the top of the frame indicate the difference in water level at high tide. (Nova Scotia Information Service)

6. "The Sentinels" guarding Hopewell Cape on the Bay of Fundy are blocks of red sandstone topped with evergreen. Several romantic Indian legends explain the weird formations, which, in fact, were carved by Fundy tides. (New Brunswick Travel Bureau)

7. A bore advances up the Petitcodiac River, New Brunswick. The front of the wave is about two feet high. (New Brunswick Travel Bureau)

8. A turbine-generator unit of the tidal power plant at La Rance, in Brittany, is anchored in its own conduit about thirty-three feet below the lowest water level. The body of the unit contains the electric generator, and one of the supporting struts is hollow to allow a man to service the generator. (Electricité de France)

whose area is about 50 square miles, or 1.40×10^9 square feet. Semi-diurnal tidal range in the bay is 6 feet. The ocean communicates with the basin by a channel only 800 feet wide and 50 feet deep. The result: 1.40×10^9 square feet $\times$ 6 feet $= 8.4 \times 10^9$ cubic feet of water must flow in or out in the course of 6¼ hours. The number of seconds in 6¼ hours is about 22,000. Thus the average volume of water which must flow through the channel per second is 8.4×10^9 feet^3 $/2.2 \times 10^4$ seconds or 3.8×10^5 cubic feet per second. The cross-sectional area of the channel is 800 feet $\times$ 50 feet $= 4 \times 10^4$ square feet. So the average speed of flow must be $\dfrac{3.8 \times 10^5 \text{ ft}^3/\text{sec}}{4 \times 10^4 \text{ ft}^2} = 9.5$ ft/sec or 6.5 miles per hour. The speed at half tide might easily be double this amount. Pilots of vessels entering or leaving this bay had better keep a close eye on their tidetables! They don't want to buck into a 10-knot tide. Even more to the point: currents of this magnitude often flow in a turbulent fashion, perhaps because of uneven bottom configuration. Under such conditions vessels may become so unmanageable as to swing around and go ashore.

In some channels flow is smooth though swift. It is an exhilarating experience to pass through the Cape Cod Canal "with the tide." The banks race by; you have the sensation of being borne along by some mysterious force.

But when you are in a channel with hidden ledges marked by navigational buoys, you have to watch out. The currents at their maximum may suck the buoys completely under and out of sight. It is frustrating—and frightening—to the navigator to miss a buoy which he is counting on and which the chart says should be there!

Awesome tidal currents occur at many places in the world. One is Unimak Pass, between two Aleutian islands. The pass joins the North Pacific Ocean and the Bering Sea. Tides in these bodies of water are out of phase, so that at times a large difference in head of water exists between the two ends of the channel.

Known to more people—through accounts which are often highly exaggerated, such as Edgar Allan Poe's—is "The Maelstrom" on the coast of Norway. Tide filling and emptying a big bay results in currents which may reach 20 knots. At speeds like this, the flow of a liquid through a channel of uneven shape creates great turbulence. Eddies form, so swift that they can be called enormous whirlpools. Tales of ships being sucked down are in the realm of fiction. Nevertheless, small craft are careful to keep clear of the channel except in periods of slack water.

In the Bay of Fundy at the city of St. John, a tide whose range reaches 25 feet at springs rushes in and out of the estuary of the St. John River. The drop takes place over a short distance, so that the so-called "Reversing Falls" are formed.

If the opening of a bay is wide, filling and emptying currents have very moderate speeds. The Bay of Fundy is a good example. Tidal currents at the mouth have been calculated; the maximum speed is probably no more than 1.6 knots. And yet at the head of this bay is found the largest tidal range in the world! Tidal energy, it has been estimated, feeds in and out of the Bay of Fundy at the average rate of about 200 million horsepower.

In shallow water, tidal currents and therefore tidal range are apt to be greatly affected by friction. Friction destroys the character of a standing wave. Implicit in the description of such a wave is unimpeded progression of two waves traveling in opposite directions—the incoming wave and the reflected wave. With friction there may still be two waves, but the amplitudes of both decrease as the waves progress. Thus, the reflected component is small and may die out completely as it approaches the mouth of the basin. The result: pure nodes no longer exist. Instead there are places where the tidal range is a minimum—but it is not zero. Also the phase difference between the tide at the head of the bay and at the mouth is lessened.

The North Siberian Shelf on the Arctic Coast is a shallow area extending some 200 miles out into the Polar Sea. The depth of the area seldom exceeds 100 feet. Frictional forces are extreme—particularly since the water is covered with pack ice during most of the year. As a result the tide on this coast is almost zero; it is measured in inches.

Chapter VII

THE TIDES AS WE SEE THEM

Tides in various parts of the world

What do actual tides look like, in various parts of the world? To what extent do they bear out the theoretical behavior we discussed earlier?

Our purpose is best served if we speak of a variety of gulfs and seas. The Red Sea is an example of a long, narrow embayment. It is so narrow, in fact, that transverse oscillations are negligible. To the south, it opens through a constricted passage into the Gulf of Aden, and thus to the open sea. To the north, it splits into two narrow canals—the Gulf of Suez and the Gulf of Aqaba. These are relatively so small that they do not effectively prevent the Red Sea from being of very simple shape. We can suppose, then, that the tide of the Red Sea is a superposition of a co-oscillating tide and a direct tide due to the action of the tide-generating forces on the waters of the sea itself. Straightforward calculations can be made to predict the magnitude of each tidal component.

Figure 44 shows the Red Sea in outline, and the location of certain ports. In Table 2 are listed, for the semi-diurnal tide, the observed and theoretical values of rise and fall at various places. Calculations are based on the behavior of a simple basin whose size and average depth are those of the Red Sea. The agreement is

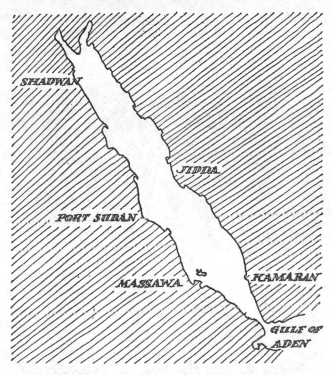

Fig. 44 The Red Sea.

good. We can say with some confidence that in general we understand these tides.

The Bay of Fundy (see Figure 45) is like the Red

TABLE 2

Place	Height of Tide (cm)	
	Observed	Calculated
Shadwan	25.1	25.4
Jidda	7.9	5.6
Port Sudan	1.6	1.0
Massawa	34.8	25.5
Kamaran	32.5	30.0

Sea in that it is long and straight-sided and the end separates into two narrow areas, Chignecto Bay and Minas Basin. But it is much smaller (160 miles long), and differs in another important respect: the mouth is

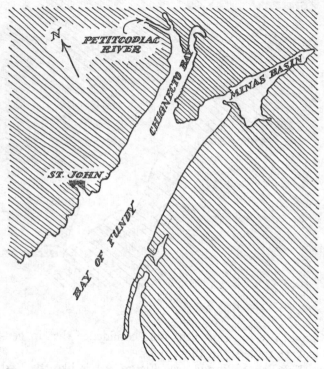

Fig. 45 The Bay of Fundy.

extremely wide. Tidal range at the opening is large but not unusual—about 9.5 feet at springs. A striking increase occurs toward the head of the bay. At St. John the range is already 25 feet. Near the end of Chignecto Bay it is 46 feet, and at the end of Minas Basin, 51 feet. There is no doubt that a standing wave in the form of a co-oscillating tide exists. Tremendous amplification occurs through resonance.

In the section of photographs are emphatic pictorial statements of the range of Fundy tides. Plate 5 shows men at work on fishnets. Note the strands of seaweed caught in meshes near the top of the framework; these meshes are too fine to appear in the print. Note also that we don't see the full height of the structure!

When storms blow from the southwest, they tend to drive water toward the head of the bay. Tidal range, already enormous, can increase as much as 6 feet.

Tides on the southeast coast of the bay (the northwest coast of Nova Scotia) are somewhat higher than those directly opposite on the shore of New Brunswick. As we might expect from our earlier discussion of standing waves in a rectangular basin, this phenomenon is due to the geostrophic effect.

To follow the advancing tide on the usual beach is something like snail-watching. You don't have to move fast to keep up with what you are observing! In the Bay of Fundy, however, you'd get more exercise. Water depth at the mouth of the Bay of Fundy is roughly 300 feet. Suppose the upward slope of the bottom were constant from there to the closed end of Minas Basin, a supposition which is not true. But if it *were* true, how far would the spring tide recede? Some 30 miles. If you were out there on a stroll, and the tide started to come in—a process which takes, of course, some six hours—you'd have to stroll straight back at an average speed of 5 miles per hour to keep from drowning! The stroll would be a very fast walk—almost a run, in fact!

Now let's talk about tides in the Mediterranean. "But," you say, "I thought there weren't any. Wasn't this implied at the beginning of Chapter I?" Well, it is true that the tides are very small, but they involve some interesting physical phenomena.

One surprising fact, related only indirectly to the tides: the level of the Mediterranean is below that of

the Atlantic. Water in the Mediterranean ranges from
four inches (in winter) to as much as twelve inches
(in summer), lower than that of the ocean outside
Gibraltar. Why is this? It is due simply to a high rate
of evaporation in a generally warm climate. Rainfall
and inflow from rivers cannot keep up with the loss.
The net rate of loss of fresh water from the Mediterranean is estimated to be about eighty thousand tons
per second!

This can be replaced in only one way—by an inflow
of ocean water through the Straits of Gibraltar. This
current is superimposed on the strong tidal currents
which must flow through the Straits. Must flow—because on the Atlantic side there is an appreciable range
of tide and on the Mediterranean side very little.

Subtracting tidal effects, what does the inward flow
amount to? It is enormous. Measurements of current
velocity (which can be as great as four knots) give a
figure of two million tons per second! But this is vastly
more than can be accounted for by evaporation. What
is happening? The answer lies in current measurements
made not only at the surface but all the way to the
bottom of the Straits. At the lower depth, there is an
outflowing current from the Mediterranean to the Atlantic, almost as great as the incoming one near the
surface. The difference makes up for the evaporation
loss.

Geostrophic effects, it is interesting to see, occur
even in the Straits. Greater inflow of water takes place
on the south side, and greater outflow on the north.

You may have wondered about one point: there
must be a "salt unbalance" in the Mediterranean; fresh
water lost by evaporation is being replaced by ocean
water. But samples of water taken from different
depths in the Straits of Gibraltar reveal an interesting
fact. The deep outflowing current consists of water of
appreciably higher salt content than that of the water

coming in. It is estimated, in fact, that the inflow and outflow are enough to give a complete renewal of the water in the entire Mediterranean every 75 years.

But what of the Mediterranean tides? If you glance at a map of this sea (Figure 46), you will notice that

Fig. 46   The Mediterranean Sea.

it divides into basins, the western and the eastern. They are joined by the Straits of Messina and of Tunis. Observations show that tides in the Mediterranean can be represented by two systems of standing waves, one in each basin.

The system of the eastern basin seems to result only from direct action of the tide-generating forces; it has its own independent tides. Why doesn't it co-oscillate with the tide of the western basin? Measurements of currents in the Straits of Messina and of Tunis give the answer. Curiously enough, in a six-hour period during spring tides, the eastern basin gains some 48 cubic kilometers from the Aegean and Adriatic Seas and loses some 53 cubic kilometers through the Straits. Thus the total mass of water in the basin tends to remain constant, and co-oscillation is negligible.

In the western basin it is another story. Independent

tides exist, of course. In addition, energy fed in through the Straits of Gibraltar produces a co-oscillation with the North Atlantic Ocean. Agreement between observation and calculated behavior, it turns out, is unusually good.

Since Mediterranean tides are on the whole so small, it is surprising that strong currents exist in the Strait of Messina. Here, according to the Homeric legend, dwelt the six-headed sea monster Scylla. On the opposite side lurked the whirlpool Charybdis.

The currents in the Strait show that strong tidal flow can exist even when the vertical range of tide is very slight. A small part of the current, it is true, arises from differences in vertical density distribution of water in the Tyrrhenian Sea to the north and in the Ionian Sea to the south. The rest is due to tidal effects; velocities can reach 4.5 miles per hour. Turbulent flow produces gentle whirlpools. One of these is Charybdis. Nowadays, it is certainly not fearsome. Perhaps changing depths of water in the Strait over the centuries have lessened the tendency for rotational motion.

Tides in river estuaries; bores

What happens when tide enters a river? It depends on the nature of the stream, on the shape of the river mouth, and on the tidal behavior in the bay outside. Clearly, tide will not penetrate far into a swiftly flowing stream, one which has a large slope or *gradient*. But in a river like the Amazon, moving its vast water masses sluggishly along through almost flat terrain, tidal effects should be felt far upstream. Indeed they are. People have seen behavior surely related to the tides as far as 500 miles from the mouth!

That part of a river which feels tidal effects is called the *tide zone*. For most streams the length of the tide zone varies considerably with the seasons. When the river is swollen the zone decreases. High current velocities tend to suppress the tidal effects.

The depth of the river is an important factor, for it determines frictional effects. Important, too, is the width and how it changes along the river.

An interesting phenomenon in rivers is the shape of the tidal curve—that is, how the rise and fall vary with time. For the ocean this curve is symmetrical. In rivers, however, the curve loses its simplicity. Typically, the rise is faster and the fall slower. The effect can occur only if the speed of the peak of the tidal wave is different from that of the trough. This difference depends upon river depth.

In a river, tidal currents are probably more interesting than degree of rise and fall. Inevitably, the tide causes periodic reversal of the direction of river flow. Change in direction occurs *after* the water has reached its maximum or minimum height, so that there is a definite phase lag. Sometimes the local configuration causes resonance effects which result in most peculiar behavior of the currents. In the Forth River in Scotland there is a triple high water!

Water depth as one enters a river estuary always gets relatively small. Friction becomes important. Thus we can't expect the rise and fall of water level to have the character of a standing wave. Instead, it will be a progressive wave—but a progressive wave whose profile varies. As water depth changes so does the speed of propagation. If the advance is into a more and more shallow region, there comes a time when depth is comparable to the amplitude of the wave. Then an important phenomenon occurs. Parts of the wave crest go faster than does the trough. The frontal slope gets steeper; finally the wave breaks—i.e., tumbles forward upon itself.

So far, what we have said applies equally well to ordinary waves approaching an ocean beach. But the advancing tidal wave represents a "permanent" increase in water level. The breaking wall of water—called a bore—rushes upstream with a front which is sometimes almost vertical. Continually, the water in back overtakes the slower water at the foot of the wave.

Plate 7 is a photograph of the bore which goes up the Petitcodiac River at Moncton, New Brunswick. Figure 47 is a cross-section profile of the bore on a certain date, determined by measurement of water height as time went on. We see that the steep front of the wave was some two feet high, followed by

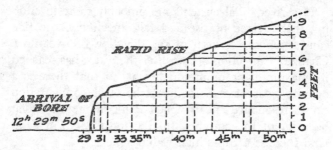

Fig. 47 Cross-section of the bore which goes up the Petitcodiac River at Moncton, New Brunswick.

a relatively rapid rise to three feet. In the course of the next twenty minutes the water rose another six feet.

Bores are more common than most people suppose. They occur in any river in which the funnelling and shallowing action bear the right relation, and at whose mouth there is sufficient tidal range. Several rivers in Europe have small bores: for example, the Seine and Gironde in France, the Severn and Trent in England. The largest bores in the world are probably those of the Amazon, and the Chien-tang-kiang in China.

The bore of the Indus in India almost brought disaster to Alexander the Great as he and his troops descended the river; they had no knowledge of the river's course. Curtius Rufus, in his *History of Alexander*, translated by Rolfe, gives a second-hand but graphic account of what happened. Alexander knew that he must sooner or later reach the ocean, but had no idea of what distance might be involved.

> . . . he sent a few men ashore in a boat, to take some of the peasants who were roving about, from whom he hoped to get more accurate information. They, after searching all the huts, at last found some hidden in them. These, when asked how far away the sea was, answered that they had never even heard of any sea; but that on the third day they could reach bitter water, which spoiled the fresh water.
>
> It was clear that this was a description of the sea by those who were not acquainted with its nature; and so the boatmen rowed on with great eagerness, and each succeeding day, as the fulfillment of their hopes drew nearer, their ardor increased.

Soon they did come to the "bitter water." They anchored at a large island in the middle of the river, and went ashore to look for supplies.

> It was nearly the third hour, when the ocean, in its regular change, began to be carried on a flood-tide into the river and pushed it back. . . . now the ships were lifted and the whole fleet was scattered, and those who had gone on shore, alarmed and amazed by the unexpected calamity, ran from every side back to the ships. But in times of confusion even haste is slow. Some were pushing at the ships with poles, others had taken their seats while they were prevented from putting their oars in place, some in their haste to sail, without waiting for those who ought to have been with them, were weakly struggling with crippled and unmanageable ships,

other ships had taken all those who rushed inconsiderately into them; and equally too great and too small numbers delayed their haste. Here some were shouting to wait, there others, to go on, and the contradictory cries of those who never demanded one and the same action had prevented the use, not only of the eyes, but also of the ears. And there was no help even in the pilots, for their voice could not be heard in the tumult, nor could their orders be carried out by the frightened and disordered sailors.

Hence the ships began to be dashed together, and the oars to be shorn off in turn, and the crews to foul one another's ships. You would have supposed, not that it was the fleet of one army, but that the fleets of two armies were engaged in a sea fight. Bows were dashed against sterns, those ships that damaged ships in front of them were in turn injured by ships behind them; from angry words they even came to blows.

It was some time before Alexander could make repairs and proceed on his way—safe by now, because he saw that the bore was a regular occurrence, and he could thereafter place his ships in sheltered spots before the wave arrived.

The first written description of the bore on the Chien-tang-kiang is probably that of Captain Moore of the Royal Navy, in command of the surveying ship *Rambler*. In September 1888 he entered the estuary, anchored, and on the morning of the nineteenth sent two small steam cutters up the river to explore. About noon the cutters experienced a tremendous flow up river which pushed them onto a shallow area where they grounded and anchored. The water rose and the current increased still more. Although the engines were kept going at full speed the boats dragged their anchors in water rushing by at an estimated 11 knots.

At slack water the cutters returned downstream and anchored at the mouth of the river. Half an hour before midnight the crews heard a distant roar to the eastward. At twelve-twenty a tremendous bore passed. Fortunately, the most violent part of the wave went by on the opposite bank. The cutters were swept upstream, dragging their anchors for three miles!

Subsequent measurements from the *Rambler* showed that shortly before midnight the difference in level between the water in the bay outside and that at the town of Haining some miles up the river was 20 feet. Something had to give! The same effect can be produced on a laboratory scale in a wave tank—a long box. You dam up some water behind a board at one end of the tank, then suddenly remove the board. A miniature but perfectly respectable bore is produced.

Junks which navigated the river had a unique system for escaping the bore. On the falling tide they grounded out on platforms built into the river bank, and there they tied up securely. At the end of each platform was a bulwark to deflect the force of the bore. As soon as the bore had passed they cast off. The water continued to rise (recall the profile of the Petitcodiac bore) and the junks were swept upstream by the racing current. Free propulsion!

An interesting feature of a large bore such as this, reported Captain Moore, is the presence of a secondary wave in the broken water just behind the crest. This wave jumps up in an irregular fashion from time to time. He saw breakers which rose as much as 30 feet above the level of the river in front of the bore. The wall of the bore itself was perhaps twelve feet high.

The bore of the Amazon is well known. There it is called the *Pororoca,* or "crashing water." Its appearance is multiple. Not only does it occur in the Canal do Norte, the northern entrance to the river, but it also branches out into numerous nearby tributaries. The explorer Martius was an onlooker at an unusual bore phenomenon at the confluence of the Guama and

Capim Rivers. He wrote (and the following is a free translation of a unique German style):

> I expected that the *Pororoca* would occur after noon, since the moon would go through the meridian one minute before midnight on this particular day (May 28, 1820). Accordingly I stationed myself on a low hillock where I could overlook the river. At half past one I heard downstream a tremendous roaring like the thundering of a great waterfall. After a quarter of an hour a water wave appeared, about 15 feet high. It extended across the whole river. The wall of water came forward with terrible speed. Flood continually poured down from the crest, always replaced by the rising water behind. In some spots behind the main wave the surface was depressed by six to twelve feet, but then quickly rose again.
>
> While I, benumbed with astonishment, watched this revolt of the waters, the surface suddenly sank, leaving small eddies. But hardly had the uproar of this first onset died away than the waters reared up again. Another living waterfall passed, making the shores tremble. Dividing into two branches, it went up both rivers and soon passed out of my sight.
>
> The whole spectacle had been the work of scarcely half an hour. The waters (curiously enough, unmuddied) gradually regained their calm. Soon, the ebb tide began.
>
> Before the *Pororoca* appears, the Indians bring their canoes to the shore and make them fast by lines carried high in the trees.

Most tidal rivers are more serene. The flow in and out is smooth. An unexpected consequence of the reversal of direction exists, however. In the normal course of its flow a river forms a well-defined channel. The character of the channel may change with the months or the years, but for short periods it is relatively stable. Its shape is determined, by the laws of hydrodynamics, for current flowing in a certain direction through a bed of given configuration.

Not so with reversing currents. For a current *coming in* to the estuary the river channel is not a suitable one. The inflow creates its own new path; thus an instability in the river bed exists. All sorts of shoals and bars are formed, which typically shift rapidly as time goes on. A tidal estuary is a worrisome place for pilots of vessels wishing to enter!

On an incoming tide, the rising salt water often pushes back the fresh water. The result: even the current in regions above the salt water zone is reversed. We have a "fresh-water" tide—and, in some parts of the world, an interesting economic consequence. Rice growers must flood and drain their fields at intervals. If they cultivate beside a river with a fresh water tide, they can—with the help of suitable ditches and barriers—control the process as they please.

Practical considerations; harbors and docks; coastlines

Those of us familiar only with ports of North America fail to realize the tidal problems in Europe. Many of the chief harbors in England and on the Continent have great tidal ranges. At Liverpool and Bristol, for example, spring tides may bring rise and fall of 30 feet or more.

With tides of this magnitude all sorts of problems arise. Cargo handling becomes very difficult. Mooring lines have to be tended constantly. Furthermore, pilings supporting a pier must be tall indeed if the deck of the pier is to be 10 feet above the highest tide level and if there is to be sufficient water depth—say 25 feet—at low tide to accommodate ships lying alongside the wharf.

You might say, "At high tide, bring the ship into shallow water alongside the pier and let her ground out." But naval architects would wring their hands in anguish. The process might be feasible for small, stubby vessels. Ordinary ships, however, simply lack sufficient longitudinal stiffness for this sort of thing. They cannot withstand stresses created by lying on a bottom unless the bottom is absolutely flat and of uniform hardness. Such a bottom is difficult to find or to create.

The answer has been to build a *dock*. This word is often misused as synonymous with wharf or pier. Strictly speaking, a dock is an area of impounded water. The level is kept approximately constant, independent of tidal action. An exception is the *dry dock*. Here there are gates which close after a ship has floated in. The enclosure is then pumped out; the ship comes to rest on specially prepared supports. Work on the hull can easily be done.

A *wet dock* also has gates, usually double "lock gates." Typically, the area within is large, so that dozens of ships can be accommodated. By the use of the lock gates, vessels can enter or leave at any time of the tide. The gates operate exactly as those in canal locks. Use of the locks does, it is true, deplete the water in the basin, but the loss can be remedied by pumping if necessary.

Ships can lie in a wet dock, protected from winds and waves and currents, and handle their cargoes in an efficient manner.

One other solution to the problem of high rise and fall has been the *landing stage*. This is a structure which rests on floating pontoons and thus goes up and down with the tide. Vertical posts driven into the bottom keep it in place; the stage slides up and down on these posts. Bridges with flexible mountings connect the structure to the shore. At Liverpool there is a landing stage twenty-five hundred feet long and eighty feet wide. At the Tilbury docks in London is a similar stage, somewhat shorter. Depth of water alongside is thirty-five feet even at low tide, so that liners of twenty thousand tons can berth there.

The famous "Mulberry Harbor" built at Arromanche off the Normandy coast during World War II included the use of an enormous landing stage.

Along the ocean shore, land and sea are locked in constant warfare. Waves with their surging energy eat voraciously at the soil; even solid rock yields slowly to the assault. Spoils of battle are usually deposited nearby to form sandbars or other shoal areas.

What has the tide to do with this conflict? It extends the field of battle. If tidal range is considerable, waves can unleash their energy over a wide stretch of beach. The whole character of the shore is different from that of a lake, no matter how large.

The tide also modifies river mouths. Without a tide, material brought down by the stream tends to deposit close inshore. If the estuary has significant tidal flow, however, the material is usually swept farther out to sea and perhaps is dispersed by currents parallel to the shore to form a complicated system of shoals.

Another effect of the tide is important. Harbors in northerly latitudes tend to become choked with ice in winter. Icebreakers can keep channels open if the ice is not too thick, but it means a constant battle. In these regions a significant rise and fall of the tide is a blessing. Continually cracked into flows, the ice departs on a falling tide, carried along by the outgoing current. New York Harbor is open throughout the winter, while regions farther up the Hudson, though still filled with salt water, are entirely icebound.

This is not the place to make more than a passing remark on the biological consequences of the tides. The subject could command a volume in itself, for the tidal flats of the sea support a unique spectrum of marine life, plant and animal. Here exist creatures whose mode of existence demands a cyclic exposure to sea and to air, or at least an environment where typical foods are available as a result of tidal action. The reader of this book will enjoy some of the excellent works on marine biology, written for the layman in these matters, which have appeared in recent years.

Effects of atmospheric disturbances

No discussion of tides as they are observed is complete without some mention of barometric effects. Whatever the calculated tables may predict for a particular tide, the actual height or depth—or even the associated currents—may differ considerably. We've already mentioned the effect of wind in piling up water masses, and how the most destructive effect of hurricanes is usually that of the wind-driven water and not of wind alone.

Now we should ask more about the effect in bays and gulfs of changes in atmospheric pressure. The sea is very sensitive to such changes. After all, it is easy to understand the principle that the height of water in a given area is related to air pressure, which pushes down on the water with a force of about 15 pounds per square inch, or over 1 ton per square foot. On a square mile of ocean this means a total downward force of over 30 million tons! If, because of local meteorological conditions, neighboring areas experience greater or less force, changes in sea level are to be expected. Under an area of low barometric pressure, for example, the surface will rise, since water will flow into the region from nearby places of higher pressure.

Don't get the idea, however, that because of the enormous total vertical forces involved the water level is subject to large variations. Remember that we are dealing only with *differences* in barometric pressure, and these differences are small compared to the total.

A relative change of a few tenths of an inch out of 30 inches is not large. As pointed out in Chapter I, a change of one inch in a mercury barometer corresponds to a variation in sea level of about 13 inches.

But what really counts is how the varying force is applied. Is it the result of a localized meteorological condition, and is the associated air mass moving or stationary? If it is moving, how fast? And what is the size of the water basin, and its depth?

The point is this: if the atmospheric disturbance is moving at a speed comparable to that of the regular tidal wave in the region, a large effect might be expected—particularly if the speed corresponds to that of a resonant condition. Differential equations describing forced tides due to astronomical tide-generating forces are identical with those describing forced tides due to a traveling atmospheric disturbance.

Meteorological stations in England on July 20, 1929, observed an atmospheric "front" moving northward at about 40 miles per hour. Accompanying the front was a large and sudden change in barometric pressure. The discontinuity created an abrupt variation in water level. As a result, a single very large wave was formed which eventually struck the Sussex coast, doing considerable damage on the beaches.

Tides in the open ocean

In Chapter IV we saw how hard it is to calculate tides theoretically for large bodies of water. Even for artificial oceans of the simplest shape the problem is almost insoluble.

If we wish to study tides in an actual ocean only one approach is realistic. We set up on the shores of this ocean, and on its islands, as many tide-observing stations as possible. If open-ocean observations are also available, so much the better. We obtain an enormous quantity of data. This we feed into a computer, which can then provide us with the amplitude of each harmonic tidal component. The rest of the operation is essentially a game. We choose a particular tidal constituent (in the Atlantic, for example, a semi-diurnal type is by far the most common in most locations). We then try to invent a system of progressive or standing waves, or a combination thereof, to explain the observations. At the same time we draw a system of cotidal lines, including any amphidromic points we may suspect are present. From our speculations we can predict tidal currents in the open ocean, and check to see if such currents have actually been measured.

We don't neglect basic theory entirely. It tells us in advance, for example, that only certain forms of cotidal lines and amplitudes are possible. Theory strengthens the picture we create. If on the basis of observation we have a choice of two quite different interpretations, pure theory can perhaps tell us which is by far the more probable. But it can do little for us in addition.

The semi-empirical interpretation, based as it is on observations taken mostly along the shore, has a great weakness. Knowing amplitudes along the coasts, how can we possibly extrapolate these data across the vast reaches of the ocean with any certainty? Modern midocean instrumentation on the survey ships is a great help, but it cannot supply us with all the information we seek.

A great deal of thought has been given to the problem, however. Certain general statements are possible. Those about the Pacific are mostly negative, to the effect that Pacific tides are the least understood. The vast expanse of the Pacific, its complicated shape, the unsatisfactory distribution of observation stations—all make statements about its tidal behavior hazardous. We do know that near the center of the Solomon Islands is a region with *no* semi-diurnal lunar tides.

Here, then, must be an amphidromic point for this constituent. A spring tidal range of about 5 inches is due to the solar semi-diurnal component.

Study of the Atlantic is more fruitful. In one sense this ocean is like a huge bay, open at the south and essentially closed at the north. Early workers postulated that Atlantic tides could be explained as co-oscillations with tides in the unobstructed Antarctic Ocean. Observations have shown, however, that this theory is not valid. The Atlantic is apparently big enough to develop its own tides.

Various workers have presented, for the Atlantic, several different pictures of possible combinations of progressive and standing waves, longitudinal and transverse. No model has stood completely the test of comparison with the increasing number of coastal observations.

Again, however, we may make certain general remarks. Unlike the other oceans, the Atlantic has a predominance of semi-diurnal tides. Diurnal tide range is commonly less than 15 inches. For the semi-diurnal tide there seems to be an anti-node crossing the ocean from the eastern tip of Brazil to West Africa. Near the southern coast of Puerto Rico in the Caribbean, there is probably an amphidromic point. It is interesting that from here north along the United States coast and all the way to Newfoundland there is almost no difference in phase. Thus in open waters high and low tides occur almost simultaneously over the whole stretch. (There are local deviations, of course, in certain bays and river estuaries.) This *simultaneity* by no means exists on the shore of the eastern North Atlantic. The phase changes rapidly as one goes north along that coast. Thus we assume that there must be a definite amphidromic point well offshore in the North Atlantic Ocean. Figure 48 shows a chart of proposed cotidal lines for the North Atlantic.

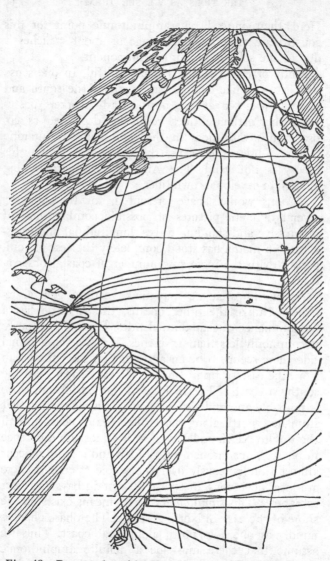

Fig. 48 Proposed cotidal lines for the North Atlantic.

Chapter VIII

POWER FROM THE TIDES

Origin of tidal power, and how the power is dissipated

To a bather stretched idly on the warm sand, the coming of the tide hardly suggests vast power. The sea is calm; as the hours pass the water's edge inches its way up the beach, then down again.

Is not tidal energy a negligible factor in the scheme of things? All along, we have emphasized how very small are the tide-generating forces compared with other forces which operate in our planetary system.

Very small they are, and yet such is the scale of the cosmos that tidal effects result in an energy dissipation —in the oceans, the atmosphere, the "solid" earth— which is enormous. Enormous, that is, in terms of man's measure of energy. Energy of the tides is continuously being dissipated at a rate whose order of magnitude is a billion horsepower!

As we shall see in Chapter XI, this vast power output comes at the expense of the kinetic energy of the earth-moon system. Part of the kinetic energy exists in the rotation of the earth on its own axis; loss of this energy means slower rotation, and a consequent lengthening of the day. There is abundant evidence that the earth is slowing. We shall examine this evidence later.

But what becomes of this awesome expenditure of

power? The law of the conservation of energy says that
the lost kinetic energy must appear in some other form.
The loss takes place in frictional effects and therefore
appears ultimately in the form of heat. Many oppor-
tunities exist for such effects: viscous forces in the
fluid interior of the earth, nonelastic properties of the
solid parts of the earth which result in the phenomenon called hysteresis, and frictional loss experienced by
tidal currents in the seas and the atmosphere.

At present, no one can assign relative weights to
these various processes. Only the ocean tidal currents
lend themselves to direct observation. One might hope
to make an intelligent guess about them. But they
occur throughout the world in most complicated forms.
They flow in depths which vary greatly; their velocities
change hourly and monthly; they move over bottoms
which may be rough or smooth; internal turbulence,
even without contact with land, is always present. To
assess energy loss due to tidal currents is, as you see,
almost impossible. Only the roughest sorts of estimates
have been attempted.

Harnessing the tides

Whatever the energy in the ocean tides, it is enormous. Can we somehow get power from this energy?
Can we, in other words, construct a system whose end
result is to change into some other form of energy,
power which would otherwise have been dissipated in
tidal friction?

Here is a challenge to you, before you read further.
Imagine yourself an engineer, asked to devise ways of
harnessing tidal power for the generation of electric
current. How many methods can you think of? Write
them down, and for each plan some suitable machinery.

Probably the most unsophisticated approach—almost childish, as it turns out—would be to say, "All

right, the tide goes up and down. Build some large floating object—an enormous, heavy, rectangular barge. Let
the tide lift it. Have a supporting structure overhead
with steel cables wound around drums; let the ends of
the cables drop vertically to eyes in the deck of the
barge. As the barge descends on a falling tide, the
cables will turn the drums. With suitable step-up gearing, the turning shafts of the drums could rotate an
electric generator."

For his own amusement, the author figured out how
much power could reasonably be expected from such
an arrangement. Take one of the largest floating objects in existence—say a modern oil tanker weighing
100,000 tons, or 2×10^8 pounds. Place it where the
tidal range is extreme. In descending through a distance of, say, 40 feet, work of 2×10^8 lb $\times$ 40 ft $=$
8×10^9 foot-pounds will be done. Since power is the
rate of doing work, we must divide this figure by the
time involved, which is roughly $6\frac{1}{4}$ hours, or 2.25×10^4
seconds. Then

$$\frac{8 \times 10^9 \text{ ft-lb}}{2.25 \times 10^4 \text{ sec}} = 3.55 \times 10^5 \text{ ft-lb/sec}$$

To convert this number into horsepower, we recall
that one horsepower is 550 foot-pounds per second.

$$\frac{3.55 \times 10^5 \text{ ft-lb/sec}}{550 \text{ ft-lb/sec per hp}} = 647 \text{ hp}$$

This is the *average* power output to be expected during
the $6\frac{1}{4}$ hours. It assumes no frictional loss in the
machinery.

The mountain has labored mightily and brought
forth a mouse. Four ordinary automobile engines could
do the same job! Furthermore, they could do it around
the clock, whereas our mechanical monstrosity would
work only during a falling tide.

Our approach to the problem of power from the

tides has been too naïve. We failed to recognize that since tidal rise and fall are so small, the secret of significant power generation is to process large quantities of water. We must, in other words, allow a great volume of water to descend through whatever tidal difference in levels is available or can be made available. The water, as it descends, must do work—say by turning a waterwheel.

Ancient tidal power installations

Waterwheels, at least in their simpler forms, have been known almost from the dawn of history. Ancient Egyptian drawings show paddlewheels dipping into the current of the Nile. Buckets attached to their rims lifted water above the level of the bank, to dump into sluices and thereby irrigate fields. It is not surprising that where swift tidal currents exist they have sometimes been used to turn wheels—though in Europe and America the power has ordinarily been used for other purposes, such as grinding corn.

Paddlewheels are rather inefficient devices; a much better machine is the typical overshot waterwheel, which can be installed wherever a head of water naturally exists or can be created by a dam. Roughly speaking, the term *head of water* means simply the available difference in levels of water between which the waterwheel works. It is the amount by which the water behind the dam stands higher than that at the foot of the dam.

In a few places a natural head of water exists along the ocean shore, where tidal currents must enter and leave a bay through a narrow opening in the rocks. More often, a dam is built across the mouth of a tidal basin. A typical example of such a power installation —used for grinding spices—was "Slade's Mill" in Chelsea, Massachusetts. Here four waterwheels generated about fifty horsepower when the full head of tide existed.

Assessment of tides as an effective source of power

Many drawbacks are inherent in the use of tidal power. One is the lack of a large head of water. Another—and worse—is the inconstancy of what head there is. Power nowadays is demanded almost solely for the generation of electricity, a demand which varies somewhat with the hour of the day and the day of the week, but which is never below a minimum value for a given region. Tidal power—unless special arrangements can be made, as we shall see later—is obviously available for only a fraction of each day.

So perhaps it is not surprising that the development of tidal power plants has languished in favor of ordinary hydroelectric installations on rivers, where dams are usually easier to build, and where a constant head of water can be maintained. Rivers themselves, of course, have inconstant flow. But if there is a sufficiently large reservoir behind the dam, the operators can "average out" the flow. If the reservoir is too small, one can (a) install only enough generating capacity for the minimum seasonal flow of the river or (b) draw water from the reservoir only for short periods of the day, when a demand for *peaking power* exists. Peaking power is that extra power necessary for times of high electrical consumption—during times of day when both industrial and domestic demands are large, or during hot days in summer when use of air conditioners represents an enormous load.

If tidal power is not constant, why not use it for peaking purposes? Alas, the tides are on a lunar cycle, whereas man lives on a solar cycle. Only by coincidence would tidal peaking power become available at the right time.

But one can look at the thing from another point of view. For a conventional thermal power plant—burning coal, or oil, or natural gas—the capital cost is ordinarily a small fraction of that for a hydroelectric installation of the same capacity. Fuel costs are high, however, whereas water comes free. For certain regions where fuel is particularly expensive, a system in which a tidal plant complements a thermal plant now turns out to be economically attractive. Output of the thermal plant can be reduced, and fuel saved, while the tidal plant is operating.

The word *now* is significant. Only in recent years has imaginative hydraulic engineering created machines and structures which lend themselves to the special problems of the tidal power plant.

Perhaps you are puzzled by this statement. After all, has not a tremendous technology for hydroelectric plants existed for some time? Yes, but there are subtleties in tidal power generation which do not appear in ordinary waterpower installations. One we have already mentioned: the head of water is always small. Typical vertical-shaft watermotors are not feasible, since their use means loss of a few precious feet in the effective head of water.

Furthermore, the head of water is constantly changing, and in fact reverses itself every six hours. For the simplest cycle—that of the ancient tidal mills—this presented no problem. These mills functioned merely on the outgoing tide, and could therefore operate only twice in twenty-four hours, for a few hours each time. In a modern tidal plant, however, power must be generated both on the rising and on the falling tide since the output per day is thus doubled. (This statement applies to the ordinary situation, in which the generating equipment is located in a dam across the mouth of a single estuary. The possibilities presented by the "double pool" system will be discussed later.)

Design requirements for an efficient tidal power installation

How then shall we design our waterwheel, or in modern terms our *turbine?* Since the head of water is small, we must allow large quantities to flow through *horizontal* channels in the dam. As the water flows, it must impinge on the blades of a turbine whose shaft is also horizontal, and on which is mounted the rotor of an electric generator. But water flows both ways as the tide goes through its cycle. How shall we manage this? Simple enough! Make the blades of the turbine reversible!

Another difficulty arises. Electric generators must run at constant speed; they are electrically "locked in" with the generators in other stations of the power network. The effective tidal head is constantly changing, however, and the speed of the water impinging on the turbine blades varies correspondingly. How do we keep the turbines from slowing as the head decreases? We have our answer already. By designing the turbine blades to be reversible, we have also made it possible to adjust their pitch, or angle with respect to the flow of water. As water speed decreases, the blades are set flatter. The power output is reduced, but the shaft maintains its necessarily constant speed. Automatic machinery controlled by a computer can take care of the whole business; no human factor need be involved.

One difficulty is inescapable. The maximum head is small, so the dam is not high. Channels through the dam cannot be of large diameter. The size of the turbine and therefore its power output are limited. The only solution: install many channels and many turbines. This is too bad, for it means violation of a basic engineering maxim that the bigger a machine the more efficient it is.

The power plant at La Rance

At the time of this writing only one large-scale tidal power plant exists. So far as the author is aware, no other is even under construction, though some proposals are being vigorously pushed. The existing plant, newly completed, is in a barrier built across the mouth of La Rance estuary in Brittany. The design follows the basic principles we have been discussing.

The estuary, shown in Figure 49, lies between the towns of St. Malo and Dinard. It has an area of about nine square miles, and is located in a region of ex-

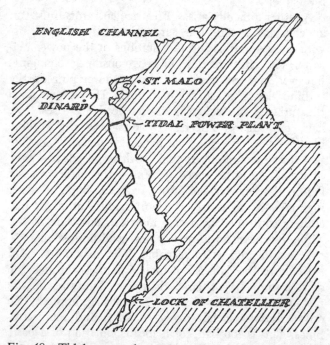

Fig. 49 Tidal power plant across the mouth of La Rance estuary in Brittany.

ceptional tidal range. The basin extends inland some thirteen miles.

Calculations show that usable tidal energy is proportional to the area of the basin involved and to the square of the amplitude of the tide. The maximum tidal range at La Rance is 44 feet. For these equinoctial tides, water flows in or out of the estuary at the maximum rate of 630,000 cubic feet per second. (This is three times the flow of the Rhone River in flood.) A useful volume of over six billion cubic feet is created.

The barrier was built at a point where the channel is 2500 feet wide. Rocks two miles downstream at the mouth of the estuary protect the works from ocean storm waves.

The installation consists of four main parts: the dam, the power plant, locks for navigation, and a barrage of sluice gates to accelerate the filling and emptying of the basin. Much geological reconnaissance was done beforehand. Borings revealed a substratum chiefly of gneiss, covered in places by thin layers of sand and gravel. The deepest water encountered was 39 feet at lowest tide, and 83 feet at maximum tide. The engineering difficulties faced were substantial but not formidable. Design of the dam involved an unusual factor, of course—the structure must be able to withstand pressure from both directions!

Before construction was started, hydraulic engineers built a working model of the whole estuary. Everything —the basin with all its contours, the proposed dam and associated works, and the tides themselves—was reproduced with the greatest fidelity. The model showed the intensity and direction of currents to be expected, and helped enormously with various aspects of the planning.

To get a "dry field" so that foundations of the different structures could be placed on bedrock, the working areas were surrounded by a string of caissons. The caissons were linked with watertight joints, and the enclosure they formed was then pumped dry. An engineering operation of this magnitude is not done quickly; some six years were needed for completion of the whole enterprise.

Vanes 33 feet high and 49 feet wide control water flow through the sluices. They, too, must resist pressure from both directions. Unlike gates in ordinary dams, which are moved only a few times a year, the vanes at La Rance are in almost constant motion. The reason: for the most efficient generation of power there must be a continuous and very close control over the water level within the basin.

The power plant, of reinforced concrete, looks inside like a vast tunnel, 1200 feet long. It contains all the control equipment. The arched roof gives the structure rigidity to resist water pressure from either side. Traveling cranes within the tunnel service the generating units. Each unit lies in its individual conduit beneath the floor; the bottom of the conduit is some 33 feet below the lowest water level. Figure 50 shows the structure in cross-section. It is interesting that at high water an observer outside and at some distance sees only a thin white line projecting above the surface of the bay. This is the roof of the power plant; everything else is submerged! To give some idea of scale: each conduit is 174 feet long, and its cross-sectional area at either end is some 1000 square feet. There are twenty-four of these conduits.

Construction of a project such as this had to wait upon design and development of a most unusual and ingenious device—the "bulb-type" turbine-generator unit which can also act as a pump. The device resembles, on an enormous scale, a short, fat torpedo. It is entirely surrounded by water. The body of the torpedo contains the electric generator, and the propeller exactly fits the constricted throat of the conduit (see

Figure 50). Struts projecting radially inward from the walls of the conduit support the unit. One of the struts is hollow, and large enough for a man to climb down a ladder from the control room into the

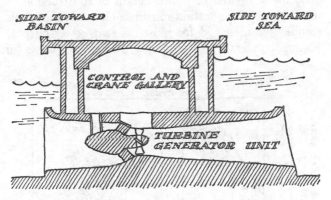

Fig. 50   Cross-section of the tidal power plant.

interior of the bulb to perform servicing (see Plate 8).

Design studies on the device were started in 1952. Smaller models of differing characteristics were installed in existing dams, and hydraulic circuits were constructed so that the units could be tested with water going both ways. In 1955 sizable units were set up in an abandoned lock system at St. Malo in order to test under actual tidal conditions.

The machines which evolved and which are now installed at La Rance each have a generating capacity of 10,000 kilowatts. The propellers, with a diameter of 17.5 feet, turn at 94 revolutions per minute. Inside the bulb, air pressure is kept double that of the normal atmosphere. The result: better cooling of the generator. At atmospheric pressure the output is limited to 7500 kilowatts, showing the great importance of proper temperature control.

The units generate power at 3.5 kilovolts. Step-up

transformers increase this voltage to 225 kilovolts; the current then enters three transmission lines which leave in different directions to link with the French national power grid.

So much for the technical details of construction. A most fascinating question remains: How can the whole complex be managed for most efficient power output? Figure 51 shows the sequence of various phases of

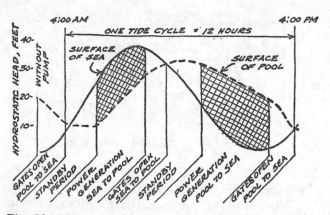

Fig. 51 Phases of operation of tidal power plant without pumping.

operation when no pumping is done. Sea level is denoted by the solid line; it is essentially a sine curve. Level within the basin is shown by the dashed line. A crucial aspect is the vertical difference in height of these two curves, i.e., the head of water. When it is appreciable, power generation is possible. The cross-hatched sections represent the times of turbine operation.

The sequence is as follows: as the ocean starts to rise from its minimum level and the head decreases to the point where efficient generation is no longer possible, the turbines are shut down, but the sluice gates open to allow continuing outflow from the basin. When basin and sea are at the same level, all gates are closed and there is a waiting period until sufficient head builds up. Then power generation begins, and continues until the combination of decreasing sea level and increasing level in the basin results in too little head. The turbines are stopped, but the sluice gates allow further filling of the basin. When levels within and without are equal the gates are closed and there is a waiting period until sea level falls sufficiently to create a new head—this time in the opposite direction. Meanwhile the blades of the turbines have been reversed and a new cycle of power generation begins, continuing until the head is again no longer adequate.

We have referred to the fact that the bulb units can also act as pumps. If power from outside the plant is fed into the generator, it is no longer a generator but a motor! It can then drive the turbine blades to act as a pump forcing water through the conduit, just as the motor of an electric fan turns the blades to create a stream of air.

But under the circumstances, what is the advantage of pumping? The answer is a little subtle but not too hard to see. Figure 52 is like Figure 51, but with the superposition of a dotted line which shows the basin level as it can be managed if pumping is done. We see that the cross-hatched area, and therefore the amount of power generated, is appreciably increased. Part of each waiting period is used for pumping—in one part of the cycle for building up the basin level, in the other part for lowering it. In both cases the available head is increased.

You can't get something for nothing, though. Since the efficiency of any machine is less than 100 percent, don't you end up with a net *loss* of energy? No, for the following reason. As you can see from the graph, one always pumps against a small head. The water pumped

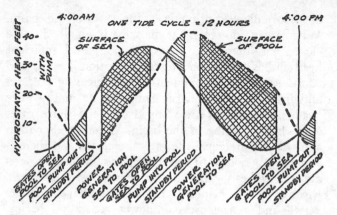

Fig. 52 Phases of operation of tidal power plant with pumping.

will later be used at a much greater head, however. Here we have the key to the worth of pumping. Another, and not altogether minor, factor is that electric energy has different monetary values at different times of day. During hours of low usage, extra power is available at reduced rates. (You already know this if your home has a clock-operated electric water heater on a separate meter.) When a waiting period at a tidal plant occurs in these hours, pumping becomes particularly rewarding.

There are several variables, as you see: basin level, sea level, value from hour to hour of energy generated and of energy bought for pumping. Proper operation of a tidal plant for maximum efficiency requires a constant and rather complicated calculation of all factors involved. The result of this running calculation must be continuously translated into control of the various components: the vanes of the sluice gates, the pitch of the turbine propeller blades, the starting and stopping of generating or pumping cycles. The whole situation calls for a computer-controlled operation, and in the plant there is indeed a computer programmed not only to perform the necessary calculations but also to control all components according to the results of the calculations.

In each of the 24 conduits at La Rance is a turbo-generator of 10,000 kilowatts capacity. Maximum power output is therefore 240,000 kilowatts. An ordinary hydroelectric plant running continuously at this capacity would produce 2100 million kilowatt-hours per year. The annual energy output at La Rance is about 540 million kilowatt-hours without pumping, and an additional 130 million with pumping. The figures starkly underline the nonconstant output of a tidal power plant. Note well, however! This is an *assured production*. There are no dry years for a tidal installation! And no worries about damage from disastrous floods.

Proposal for Passamaquoddy Bay

La Rance is the only large-scale tidal plant in operation. What of possibilities elsewhere? The proposed Passamaquoddy project is probably the best known. Passamaquoddy Bay lies near the mouth of the Bay of Fundy (see Figure 53). The boundary line between Maine and New Brunswick runs through it; virtually all of the water lies in the Canadian portion, however. Any plan would involve full cooperation of both the United States and Canadian Governments.

There is no doubt that the area is most attractive for the production of tidal hydroelectric power. Average range of tide is about 18 feet, and spring tides can reach 25.7 feet. The flow is enormous. Some 70 billion cubic feet of water enter and leave. (Compare with La Rance's 6 billion cubic feet.)

The power possibilities at 'Quoddy were first studied on a large scale in the 1920s by engineer Dexter P.

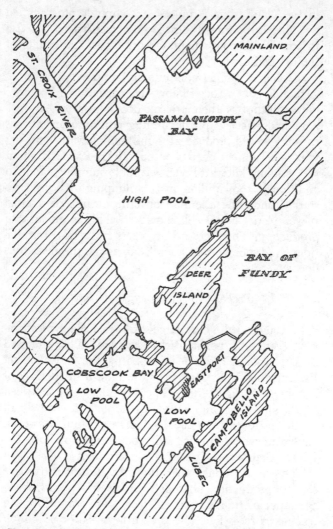

Fig. 53 Site of the proposed Passamaquoddy Bay tidal power plant.

Cooper. His plan was a "two-pool" installation. Passamaquoddy Bay and nearby Cobscook Bay would be blocked off from the ocean to create two reservoirs, between which a constant head of water would be maintained.

The project was too ambitious and costly for the times. The thirties brought the Depression, however, and with it the U. S. Government's great public works program. The Government authorized, in 1935, development of a single-pool project to use only the waters of Cobscook Bay. No international problems were involved in such a plan. But here began one of the roles of 'Quoddy—that of a political football—and the project has played this role ever since. This is not the place to search out the political ramifications of the enterprise. Let's say only that vested private power interests naturally oppose the expansion of public power facilities, and that for any project of this sort there are always those who cry "pork barrel." It is probably fair to say that no power proposals—including those on the Colorado River—have aroused more violent emotions. More importantly, as we shall soon make clear, engineers can present serious doubts about the economic feasibility of the project.

In any event, determined congressional opposition appeared immediately, and in 1937 work was suspended. Little actual construction had been done. Engineers had carried out much survey and design, however, investigations which were to be of great value in later discussion of the project.

Soon after the end of World War II, an international joint commission was formed. Its task was to review all previous reports involving production of power at 'Quoddy, and to look into the cost of a comprehensive study of a two-pool international plan using both bays. The report of the commission appeared in 1950. As a somewhat delayed result, engineers carried out extensive surveys and prepared recommendations during the period 1956–59.

One important result of the study: there was no doubt as to which scheme was better. A two-pool plan is much more efficient. Passamaquoddy Bay, with an area of 100 square miles, would be the high pool; the 40-square-mile Cobscook Bay, the low pool. Figure 54

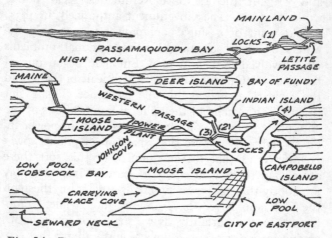

Fig. 54 Proposed power plant at Passamaquoddy Bay using a two-pool plan.

is an oblique view of the region in which most of the works would be constructed.

How to make 'Quoddy Bay into a high pool? Build dams between Deer Island and (1) the Canadian mainland, (2) Indian Island, and (3) Moose Island, on which lies the city of Eastport. Put another dam (4) between Indian Island and Campobello Island. Block off with power plant structures and dams the passage which makes Moose Island essentially a double island. Install 40 filling gates in dam (1) and 50 in that part of dam (2) which separates 'Quoddy Bay from the ocean. [The other part of dam (2) blocks off

Cobscook Bay from the ocean.] As the sea rises, open the 90 filling gates. Close them when the level of 'Quoddy Bay is that of the sea at high tide.

To make Cobscook Bay a low pool: build a dam near the town of Lubec (see Figure 53), linking Campobello Island to the U.S. mainland. Put 70 emptying gates in dam (4). Open them when, at low tide, sea level drops below the level of the low pool.

One problem at 'Quoddy is not faced at La Rance: that of large marine traffic. A single set of navigation locks would in any case not suffice, since vessels must be able to enter both the high and the low pools. Instead, four sets of locks are contemplated. One set allows entrance to 'Quoddy Bay through the passage to be closed by dam (1). A second in dam (4) and a third at Lubec will connect the ocean with the low pool. The fourth set will be located at dam (3), permitting direct passage between the high and low pools.

The proposed power plant uses the head of water existing between the two pools—about 18 feet on the average. It follows the general design principles which we discussed earlier in the chapter. Two 50-unit power-generating structures are proposed, with a total capacity of 1000 megawatts, continuous rating. For short periods of time during spring tides the generators could be operated 15 percent above their rated capacity.

Design criteria for the generating units differ somewhat from those at La Rance, for at 'Quoddy the flow through the turbines is in one direction only and the volume of water to be handled is much greater. Very large turbines are planned, with propeller diameters of some 27 feet, almost 10 feet greater than those at La Rance. Because of the lower head, however, the wheels will turn at only 40 revolutions per minute, and the generators have the same rating—10,000 kilowatts each. Figure 55 is a cross-sectional view showing a proposed design for one of the 100 generating units. The genera-

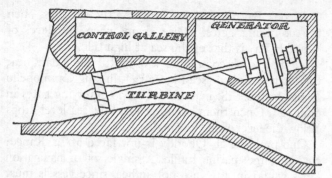

Fig. 55 Cross-section of proposed design for Passama-quoddy generator.

tor housing, as you see, is not surrounded by water as at La Rance. Powerhouse operation is fully automatic. The controlling computer would have tidal predictions at its disposal to help with its decision-making.

From the engineering point of view, the construction involved is formidable, one might even say shocking, in its magnitude. The power plant and locks are difficult enough. But the dams to create the necessary barriers are gargantuan. No less than seven miles of rock-filled dam must be built. Portions of them would be in water depths as much as 300 feet. They must be watertight, and during the final phase of their construction they must be closed in the face of tidal currents with speeds as much as 20 feet per second. The dams present design and engineering problems without precedent.

The proposed dams consist of a clay core, for watertightness, supported by rock fills on either side. Figure 56 shows such a dam in cross-section, at a point where the maximum water depth is encountered. Note the scales, both vertical and horizontal. The thickness of the dam at its base is 1400 feet, or over a quarter of a mile! The total volume of rock and clay which must

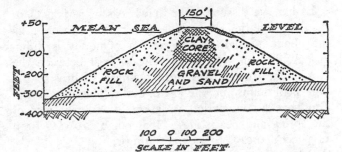

Fig. 56 Cross-section, at maximum water depth, of proposed dam at Passamaquoddy.

be moved into place to form these dams is almost inconceivable.

This description of the engineering aspect has necessarily been brief. It is enough to make clear, however, the magnitude of the undertaking. We had better return now to the international joint commission which had been studying the engineering reports. In April 1961 the commission announced that "It is evident that construction of the tidal power project by itself is economically unfeasible by a wide margin. . . . In short, the Commission finds that the tidal project, either alone or in combination with auxiliary sources, would not permit power to be produced at a price which is competitive with the price of power from alternative sources."

Despite this adverse statement, President Kennedy in the month which followed requested the Secretary of the Interior to review the report and find out what changes in any aspect of the project might make it feasible. Those who made the resulting study asked themselves: Is there a different role which a tidal plant at 'Quoddy could play? Could it operate, for example, as a peaking power installation? The necessary studies were recently completed.

Earlier, we discussed the drawbacks of a tidal plant for the generation of peaking power. But we were talking about a single-pool operation. 'Quoddy is different. A head of water would always exist between the two pools, though this head changes slightly as the high pool drains and the low one fills. The head would also have a long-period variation, of course—that of the spring and neap tides. Tidal range can vary from 11.3 feet at neaps to 25.7 at springs.

We are assured, then, of at least a certain minimum generating capacity at all times. In the language of the hydroelectric engineer, this is called *dependable* or *firm* power. All capacity at 'Quoddy in excess of the minimum—and it would be considerable—is secondary or non-firm energy. To make this greater capacity dependable, an auxiliary source of power must be available.

We might add, parenthetically, that the operation of a two-pool tidal plant has a certain elasticity which lends itself to peaking purposes. The high pool can always be filled to its maximum and the water retained at this favorable head until a time of large energy consumption in the power network. The turbines can then be started—or, if already running, their output can be drastically increased for a short period.

Where can we get auxiliary power to "firm up" 'Quoddy? One possibility is the Upper Saint John River in the extreme north of Maine. (The Lower Saint John makes its way through New Brunswick and meets the Bay of Fundy at the city of Saint John.) At present, on its upper reaches, the river churns and leaps through a series of rapids. By the inexorable laws of thermodynamics the energy lost appears simply in the form of a slight heating of the water. Why not, say some, build a dam here? Let the lost potential energy take a useful form.

The project is now known as the Dickey Dam. It

would lend itself to coordinated operation with 'Quoddy. With an installed capacity of 1000 megawatts at 'Quoddy and 750 megawatts at Dickey, proponents of the plan claim firm power output of 250 megawatts from Dickey and a dependable peaking capacity of 1000 megawatts from the combination. Since the firm output of each plant working alone would be considerably below its installed capacity, this figure for dependable peaking power seems somewhat magical. Remember, though, that both installations, being hydroelectric, can "overdraw their accounts" for a short time—the tidal plant from Passamaquoddy Bay, and the Dickey plant from the storage reservoir behind the dam. Here is the secret, then. The two could take turns in their prodigality, with Dickey providing power when the tides do not serve well.

So far so good, though as we shall see there are those who disagree. There is no disagreement about one matter, however. The spurts of water released at Dickey would result in very uneven flow in the Lower Saint John. Anguish and recrimination on the part of our Canadian friends can be anticipated. For this reason another dam creating a regulating reservoir of sufficient capacity would have to be built downstream from Dickey. Regret for the extra investment is tempered by the realization that a certain (though much lesser) amount of power could be generated at this second dam.

The Department of the Interior, in its report dated July 1963, recommended that the results of its studies be sent to Congress, as the basis for authorizing immediately both the 'Quoddy and the Upper Saint John developments. It recommended further that the Secretary of State, instructed by the President, should enter into discussions with the Canadian Government to arrange (1) the joint development of the 'Quoddy project, and (2) the sharing of power benefits from the Saint John River.

In rebuttal, private power interests engaged a firm of consulting engineers to make an appraisal of the project and of the Interior Department report. Inevitably its conclusions as to feasibility were drastically at variance with those of Washington. The appraisal points out—with some justification—contradictions, ambiguities, and misleading statements in the Government report. Its calculations show no sound economic basis for the enterprise.

The truth, as usual, probably lies somewhere in between. Both sides have undoubtedly overstated their cases.

Clearly, the whole project must be judged against the background of present power technology. And this technology is by no means standing still. Conventional thermal power plants continue to increase their efficiency, through higher steam temperatures, and also through the installation of huge turbine-generator units which are more efficient merely because of their size.

Furthermore, the role of nuclear power plants is now well understood. Were it not for the continuing improvements in conventional thermal plants, nuclear power would be competitive with power from fossil fuels. It is indeed already competitive in regions of high conventional fuel cost despite the much greater capital investment required for a nuclear reactor.

Given the more economical thermal production of power, both nuclear and conventional, those who argue for the 'Quoddy-Dickey hydroelectric complex must make a strong case. They must justify a capital investment which is breathtaking—at least 1.2 billion dollars, and very possibly a good deal more.

Another aspect: the project is an international one, but the United States would be footing the bills. One might expect that the Canadians would be delighted. If they are, they have concealed their delight rather well. The New Brunswick Government is interested, it is true, but there is talk of a purely Canadian development far up in the Bay of Fundy where tidal range is much greater than at 'Quoddy. Here, it is claimed, 900 megawatts could be generated as firm power. The cost of construction would be less than 'Quoddy's.

At the time of this writing, the Passamaquoddy project is at a standstill. Dickey Dam, however, as a separate enterprise, is being vigorously pushed by various powerful interests.

Chapter IX

TIDES IN THE EARTH

The earth, its interior and crust

We've talked at length about tides—tides involving water, that is. In what other sense may we speak of tides? How, other than in the motions of water masses, may the earth respond to the tide-generating forces?

The answers to these questions lie in the fact that there is more to the earth than just the oceans. Wherever a bit of matter lies—whether it is a molecule of nitrogen in the atmosphere, a water molecule in the ocean, a silicon ion fixed in its crystal lattice deep within the earth—the tidal forces of gravitation act upon it. But how it and its adjacent particles respond to these forces depends very much on their situation.

We've seen how fluid masses on the earth's surface react to the forces. These matters have occupied us so far in the book. What, if anything, happens to the atmosphere, and to the "solid" earth?

Many things happen. We'll postpone discussion of those having to do with the atmosphere until the following chapter. Here, let's talk of tidal phenomena in the body of the earth.

Perhaps you say, "there can't be any. We know how relatively tiny are the tidal forces. Surely their effects can only be felt in a medium—like water—which is quite free to respond to such forces. The earth itself is too rigid."

In Chapter II, when we were discussing the measurement of tide-generating forces, we met some hints that all is not well if we adopt the foregoing view. Let's speculate about what might happen if the earth does respond to (i.e., is distorted by) the tidal forces. But first let's see if what we already know of the earth's interior makes such a response likely.

The earth consists of three distinct regions: the crust, the mantle, and the core. The crust, in terms of the enormous dimensions of the earth, is a thin and fragile shell coating the sphere. It floats on the denser material beneath. Under continental areas it is perhaps 20 or 25 miles thick; beneath the oceans its thickness is appreciably less. (The latter fact led to the conception of the Mohole Project, whereby a floating drilling rig would bore through the thin crust and into the region below, which is called the mantle.) The division between the crust and the mantle, a boundary between regions of very different physical properties, is called the Mohorovicic discontinuity.

We have just spoken of the crust as floating. Perhaps this is a poor expression, for the mantle is certainly not a liquid. Rather, it is rigid, more rigid in fact than the crust. The rigidity of the earth increases downward for some 1800 miles.

Knowing as we do the total mass of the earth, and its dimensions, we can calculate its average specific gravity. The figure is about 5.52. We observe that the specific gravity of most materials in the crust is less than 3. Specific gravity deep down, then, must be considerably greater—certainly more than 5.5. One might argue that the inner part of the earth could be light, with very heavy material lying between it and the surface. Such a view is untenable on dynamical grounds; a system with this sort of mass distribution would be in a state of gravitational instability.

Is there any way to get some idea of the actual mass

distribution? Yes. We can study the *moment of inertia* of the earth.

We know that a rotating object has *angular momentum*, a quality quite analogous to that of *linear momentum*. The linear momentum of a moving object is the product of its mass and its velocity. If the object has large mass and large velocity, it is hard to stop. In the absence of any external net force on the object the momentum remains constant; it is conserved. (In essence, we have simply stated Newton's first law of motion.)

If no net external torque (twisting action) is applied to a rotating object, its angular momentum is constant. Angular momentum is defined as the product of the object's moment of inertia I and its angular velocity ω. The larger each of these quantities, the harder it is to stop the rotation or to change the direction of the rotation axis. We see that moment of inertia plays, in the matter of rotation, something of the role of mass in linear motion. But it is a more complicated thing.

Perhaps a simple thought experiment will make the idea clear. Suppose you have a slanting board, down which you propose to roll various cylinders all of the same mass, length, and diameter. One cylinder consists merely of a piece of thin-walled steel tubing. Another is a solid aluminum rod. A third is a cylinder of balsa wood; a hole has been bored lengthwise through its center and filled with a small rod of lead.

The question: which of these cylinders will take the least time to roll down the board? Remember—all weigh the same. The winner, announced in advance: the wooden rod. Second: the solid rod. Last: the thin-walled tubing. The differences in time will be significant. Why? Because the *moments of inertia* of these objects are so different. We see that the farther from the center the mass is concentrated, the greater the object's reluctance to be set rotating. Or, if it is already turning, the greater its opposition to being stopped.

Thus the moment of inertia of an object is a description both of its mass and of the radial distribution of that mass. The same experiment could have been done with balls of various construction. A thin-walled hollow ball would always be the laggard. For it, $I = \frac{2}{3}mR^2$. For a solid ball of uniform density, $I = \frac{2}{5}mR^2$. (In each case R is the radius of the ball and m its mass.)

If by some means we observe the earth's change in angular velocity resulting from a known external torque, we can figure out its moment of inertia. Then we play a game. We make various models of the earth, each with a given radial distribution of mass. For each model we calculate the equivalent moment of inertia, and compare it with the observed value until some sort of agreement is reached. Unfortunately, the result is never unambiguous. Various models may turn out to have the same moment of inertia. But at least progress can be made; aspects of the earth found from other kinds of observation can sometimes decide which model is more likely to be valid.

How do we deduce the earth's moment of inertia? The most usual method is to study the earth-moon system. Earlier, we spoke of the moon's attraction on the earth's equatorial bulge. This causes a slight variation in the direction of the earth's spin axis. The laws of mechanics relate the change to the earth's moment of inertia. It appears from the calculations that the actual value of I is about 0.83 of the value for an earth whose density is constant throughout. If this value is correct, then I (actual) equals $0.83 \times \frac{2}{5}mR^2 = 0.332mR^2$. Obviously, there is a greater concentration of mass toward the center.

Earthquakes are a great source of information about the interior of the earth. Much progress has been made in recent years in their study—the science of *seismol-*

ogy. Each 'quake gives rise to seismic waves which can proceed along the surface but also *through the whole earth.* The arrival of the waves at observing stations on the earth's surface is recorded by *seismographs.* The operating principle of the instrument is simple. A heavy mass is somehow suspended so that it is free to move relative to the frame of the seismograph. The frame is firmly fixed to bedrock. If a seismic wave arrives the rock, and therefore the seismograph, shakes. Because of its inertia, however, the heavy mass (such as the bob of a pendulum) remains at rest. The relative motion between the mass and the frame is recorded on paper wound on a drum. Clockwork turns the drum so that a continuous record is obtained.

All kinds of design refinements exist in modern seismographs. The observer can tell from what direction the wave arrived, and what kind of wave it is— longitudinal or transverse. The longitudinal or *P waves* are the faster; the transverse or *S waves* go more slowly. Another important difference: S waves, being transverse, cannot travel through a liquid unless it is very viscous. Rigid parts of the earth can transmit both types of wave. Two qualities of the earth's inner material, important to the study of earth tides, can be gotten from seismic data. One is the *rigidity* of the material, or its resistance to change of shape. The other is its *incompressibility,* or resistance to squeezing.

Suppose within the earth there are boundaries representing sudden changes of density, or rigidity, or incompressibility. Study of seismic waves can reveal them. It is a fundamental aspect of any kind of wave motion that reflection of some degree always occurs at a boundary separating regions in which the speed of the wave is different. To take an example: the speed of sound waves in air depends on temperature. It is then possible for sound waves to be reflected off the invisible boundary between a cold air mass and a warm air mass. Much of the "rolling" of thunder arises in this way.

Similarly, we observe and can study seismic waves reflected from spherical boundaries deep within the earth. These boundaries separate regions in which the speeds of seismic waves are different. How do we know that the boundaries are spherical—i.e., that they have a common center, the center of the earth? How do we know, in other words, that the distribution of density and of other properties is radially symmetric?

Seismic observations at different stations give the answer. No matter what paths the waves follow in various regions, for a given distance of travel the times are almost identical. There can be only one conclusion: whatever the earth's inner structure, it is extremely symmetrical with respect to its center.

Mathematical analysis—rather complicated, but reliable—allows us to find the speeds of the P and S waves through most of the interior. At a depth of some 1800 miles the P speed is suddenly lessened. The boundary thus defined is that of the core, a sphere of radius about 2160 miles. S waves, we find, do not travel beyond this boundary; they cannot propagate through the material of the core. We suspect then, that much if not all of the core is molten.

There is, in fact, some structure to the core itself. Part of the P wave observations can only be explained by assuming an inner core having a radius of about 800 miles. Here there is another change in P wave speed. Perhaps this region is solid; some current theories support the notion.

Speeds in the mantle of both waves are known; they increase with depth. These data, with other evidence, let us estimate specific gravity for various regions. The figure ranges from about 3.3 just below the crust to roughly 5 at the bottom of the mantle. There, at the boundary of the outer core, specific gravity jumps suddenly to around 10. For the inner core, one has to be content with an educated guess. Some evidence suggests that the figure may lie in the range of 14 to 18.

For the study of earth tides, we'd like to know as much as possible about the elastic properties of the earth. Long ago—over 100 years ago, in fact—Lord Kelvin calculated that the earth as a whole has roughly the rigidity of regular steel. (Most surface rocks have a rigidity considerably less than this.) He based his calculations on what was then known about earth tides.

More recent observations show that the rigidity of the mantle increases considerably with depth. At the bottom of the mantle the figure is twice Kelvin's value for the earth as a whole. The outer core, being fluid, has a rigidity of essentially zero.

Incompressibility of the mantle also increases with depth. But, unlike rigidity, incompressibility appears to suffer no large change at the boundary between mantle and outer core. Rather, it goes on increasing toward the center, where it may reach a value 10 times that of regular steel.

We'll soon see that another quality of the earth's material is important to our discussion. It is *elasticity*. Elasticity is a familiar concept. We say that the material composing an object is perfectly elastic if, when a distorting force is removed, the object returns exactly to its original shape—and, in the process, no energy is lost in heat or other dissipative ways.

If this perfection is not attained—if, in the process, viscous flow exists—then permanent distortion occurs and we have exceeded the *elastic limit* of the material. Time is an important factor here. Rocks which seem perfectly elastic under sudden short-term stresses may "creep" if stress is applied over a long period. We have all seen similar behavior (much exaggerated) in the case of silicone putty. A ball of this putty, thrown against a stone wall, bounces right back. The same ball, left by itself on a table, is found the next day to have sunk into a despondent heap.

Data from seismic waves indicate that the earth is almost perfectly elastic. Lack of elasticity would show up, as we shall see, in phase differences between the earth tides and the tide-producing forces.

We have said little so far about the earth's crust. The crust is indeed a remarkable thing. It is life's platform. And life exists only by a set of physical coincidences. Heat from the sun has been just enough to keep most of the earth's surface in a temperature range within which water is liquid. It is to this range that the processes of life are restricted.

Heat has also come from radioactive processes within the earth, and as "primeval heat" stored deep in the interior when the earth was formed. The thermal energy within was vital to the creation of land; volcanic activity and earthquakes lifted material above the level of the sea and made a dwelling place for land based life.

The role of volcanism is still wider. Not only did it raise the land in certain areas; it created the materials of which the crust is made, it created the oceans, it created the atmosphere. Geophysicists and geochemists have established beyond doubt the plutonic origin of our familiar environment. The materials underwent complicated processes of modification, to be sure. Nevertheless, they all came from within the earth.

Perhaps you object that volcanoes are few (at least nowadays) and spew forth little material. But ask a geologist to make a rough estimate of how much they do put out in a year. Double the figure he gives. (There is evidence of more volcanic activity in the past.) Multiply the result by 4.5 billion years (the estimated age of the earth). You will find, no doubt to your amazement, that the amount is sufficient to account for the entire earth's crust!

One aftermath of volcanism is the creation of vast systems of fractures in the crust. These fractures show up as *faults,* now mapped for most of the world. Earthquakes and volcanoes typically occur along these lines of instability. Also, measurements of earth tides in their vicinity often show strange behavior; unexpected tilting of the land may occur under the action of the tidal forces.

Nature of earth tides

By now, perhaps, we know enough of the earth's constitution to talk about the possible nature of earth tides or *body tides.* First, however, we'd better agree on what we mean by the term. It is currently used in two ways. We may be referring to the variations in the intensity of gravity, and in the direction of the vertical, which result from the tide-generating forces. Or we may mean the actual distortion of the earth which accompanies these variations. No doubt exists about body tides in the first sense; the phenomena are a direct consequence of the astronomical forces, and we have already spoken of them in Chapter II.

Whether or not the earth responds to these varying stresses by showing distortions is another matter. We'll soon examine the evidence. Suppose it turns out that distortions of the correct periodicity exist. If we can measure them, we have a potentially powerful tool to help us deduce which models of the earth's interior more resemble actuality. For each model, that is, one can predict a certain type of response to the tide-generating forces. Accurate measurement of the real distortion, therefore, would provide a frame of reference for comparison of various ideas about the earth's structure. The geophysicist, then, is the person to whom the study of earth tides means the most.

In Chapter II we described an instrument which can

detect the horizontal component of tide-generating forces: the horizontal pendulum. Were the earth completely rigid, all the readings of this instrument would agree with values of the forces calculated on a theoretical basis. If, on the other hand, the earth were entirely limp and responded fully to the forces, the apparatus would record no change as the forces varied. The surface of the earth would simply keep itself at right angles to the effective direction of gravity.

What do we in fact observe? A real effect exists, but its magnitude is less than the theoretical value. Thus the earth is not completely rigid—as of course it cannot be.

Partial tidal forces

Before we turn to the experiments which lead to these conclusions, perhaps we'd better speak a bit more about the various partial tidal forces, of their horizontal and vertical components, and of the possible response of the earth in terms of equilibrium theory.

We'll consider only the four most important of these harmonics: the M_2 lunar semi-diurnal period of 12 hours, 25 minutes, 14 seconds; the S_2 solar semi-diurnal period of 12 hours; the K_1 luni-solar diurnal period of 23 hours, 56 minutes, 4 seconds (this is the sidereal day); and the O_1 lunar diurnal period of 25 hours, 49 minutes, 10 seconds. Astronomical data allow us to calculate the amplitudes of all of these for any latitude on the earth. It is interesting to see how they do vary with latitude.

Let's look at these forces in terms of their components. First, the vertical components. Diurnal tidal forces have no vertical component at the equator, whereas here the semi-diurnal ones are at their maximum. Figure 57 shows the relative variations in gravity due to the four partial tides as latitude increases. To

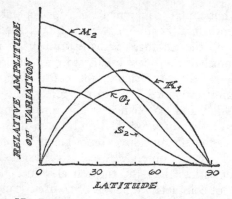

Fig. 57 Relative variations in gravity due to the four partial tides as latitude increases.

give you an idea of their magnitude: the largest effect shown, that of the M_2 tide at the equator, corresponds to a gravitational acceleration of 7.3×10^{-5} centimeters per second per second. Compare this with g, the acceleration due to the earth's gravitational field, which is some 980 centimeters per second per second! You are thereby reminded again of the relatively tiny forces with which we are dealing, and thus of the exquisite sensitivity of the instruments built to measure these forces.

Figure 57 is of great help to the geophysicist hoping to study tidal variations in gravity. They tell him not to search for diurnal tides at low latitudes (or at very high ones). Best put the observing station at 45 degrees for such periodicities. And study the M_2 and S_2 tides near the equator.

What of the horizontal components? They differ in their north-south and east-west effects, so we shall treat these directions separately.

Variations with latitude of the north-south components are shown in Figure 58. The diurnal terms are at their negative and positive maxima at the equator

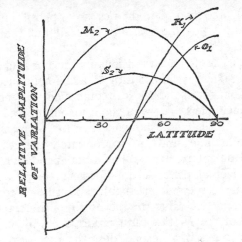

Fig. 58 Variations with latitude of the north-south components.

and the poles; the semi-diurnal ones are zero. The two effects are, as the physicist would say, 90 degrees out of phase with respect to latitude.

Figure 59 makes clear the changes with latitude of the east-west components. Again (and as we would

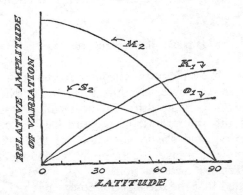

Fig. 59 Variations with latitude of the east-west components.

expect), the two periodicities are opposite in their behavior. M_2 is the main tide at all but the higher latitudes.

How large are the variations in the horizontal components? Here we must turn to a different measuring unit. Changes in the vertical component are measured with gravimeters. Those in the horizontal components, on the other hand, show up in "tilt"—variations of the plumb line—and are appropriately observed with an instrument such as a horizontal pendulum. Thus the horizontal parts of the tide-generating forces are ordinarily expressed in angular measure—seconds of arc. The largest value for the north-south components is that of the K_1 tide, and represents a tilt of about plus or minus 0.01 second. For the east-west components, that for M_2 reaches a maximum of 0.016 second.

We are beginning to get a feeling for the major effects which the tidal forces can exert on the solid earth. They are two: (1) a change in the effective *magnitude* of the earth's gravitational force, which may result in a vertical displacement of the earth's surface, and (2) a variation in the apparent *direction* of the earth's gravitational force, which can also result in distortion.

Possible physical consequences

What observable physical consequences might we expect? Here are some: a reduction in the amplitude of ocean tides, periodic drifts in the readings of gravimeters, a tilt of the crust of the earth with respect to the vertical, and elastic distortions of the crust. The last-named may take the form of tensions and volumetric expansion-contraction.

Granted that the earth is not completely rigid, could Newton's equilibrium theory apply to the deformations we shall call earth tides and which result from the tide-generating forces? Within the limits which we have already established for the validity of this theory, it can certainly be used. It should work, in fact, very much better than it does for ocean tides. The equilibrium theory is bad for the ocean because it neglects inertial effects and land configurations. These matters, as we have seen, are basic to an understanding of tides in the sea. The body tides, however, are much simpler. Earth particles can be displaced only a small amount. Equilibrium comes very soon. Furthermore, if there are oscillations, the earth can only vibrate as a sphere, and we have known the theory of such vibrations for a long time. For example, a sphere of water the size of the earth would have a fundamental oscillatory period of ninety-four minutes. But the earth is only partially liquid; it has cohesion. Calculations based on recent evidence concerning the structure of the earth give its fundamental period at about 54 minutes. The periods of the tidal forces are much greater than this. No resonances, then, with all the complications they bring! (You must realize that earth tides are just as *variable*, however, as those of the ocean. They must be, since they simply reflect the tidal forces whose intricate changes with time we have already discussed.)

Equilibrium theory, then, may be expected to work better for body tides than for ocean tides. Even here— just in case—we'd do well to study the response to long-period terms in the tidal forces, such as the lunar fortnightly, as well as to the faster variations. Measurements should be taken over a protracted time—one or more lunar years. Most effects due to random perturbations will then average out.

Suppose for the moment that the tide we are talking about *does* obey the equilibrium theory. How would our observations of the ocean tide be affected by earth distortion? Let's be specific, to the extent of thinking of a tide-measuring staff driven into the ocean bottom (see Figure 60). Here the bottom of the sea is at a level we'll call A (we are assuming for the present that the earth is completely rigid). Mean sea level is at C, and high water level at D. The tide gauge will therefore reveal a tidal amplitude $\overline{CD}$.

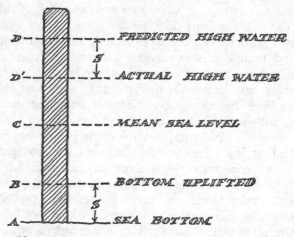

Fig. 60 A tide-measuring staff.

But what if the earth itself bulges at the beckoning of the tidal forces? Then the sea bottom will rise, say by an amount s to the level B. Does the level D of high water rise correspondingly?

Certainly not! The top of the water bulge depends only (as we saw early in the book) on a balance between the tidal forces and the gravitational force of the earth tending to make the water run back "downhill." Bulging of the earth will simply bring the sea bottom closer to the level D. The reading $\overline{CD}$ will be reduced by the amount $\overline{AB}$. High water reaches level D' on the marker, not D. (Actually, for precise work a small correction must be applied to the foregoing statement. The bulge of the earth will cause a slight gravitational effect leading to a rise of the ocean which is about one-eighth of its original range.)

Now all this is very interesting. In principle, one way to detect and measure an earth tide is then merely to compare the observed ocean tidal amplitude $\overline{CD}'$ with the value $\overline{CD}$ predicted by theory. Of course, we know that the operation is not as simple as it seems at first glance. But we are getting sophisticated about such things. We remember that we can apply the equilibrium theory only to a long-period harmonic of the ocean tide—and even then the answer is not very reliable. The calculated $\overline{CD}$ only approximates the real situation. Also, for our measurements we must choose observing stations located essentially in the open ocean —preferably on isolated islets. To separate out the partial tide by harmonic analysis and thereby get $\overline{CD}'$ will require observations extending over a long time.

Unfortunately, the longer the period of the partial tide the harder it is to find its amplitude accurately. In a nutshell, both $\overline{CD}$ and $\overline{CD}'$ are difficult to get with any assurance. In the early days of tidal study various people showed vast patience in the task. Their results differ over a range so great, however, that it is clear the difficulties are almost insuperable. Values obtained for the ratio $\overline{CD}'$ to $\overline{CD}$ varied from 0.42 to 0.84. This despite the fact that high water came at the times predicted by equilibrium theory, so that in principle the method is justified. The approach, then, has only historical interest. Indirect effects, of which we shall speak shortly, probably explain the spread of results.

We had better turn to data provided by sensitive horizontal pendulums and gravimeters. Let's speak first of the former instrument.

What is the effect of the horizontal components of the tidal forces? They cause, as we have seen, a change in the direction of the earth's apparent gravitational field—reflected, for example, in the way a plumb line hangs. The horizontal pendulum allows us to measure such changes with considerable accuracy. If the earth were rigid and had no oceans or atmosphere, there would be no point in doing experiments, however. The results would already be predicted from the calculation of the astronomical forces; they were, in fact, presented in Figures 58 and 59.

If, on the other hand, the earth does yield to the tide-generating forces, the behavior of the pendulum will differ. In Chapter II we described a typical horizontal pendulum which can measure almost infinitesimal changes in the vertical. If two of the instruments are used, at right angles to one another, effects due to both the north-south and east-west components can be detected and combined. In Figure 61 we see how the

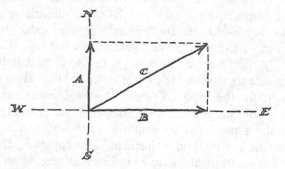

Fig. 61 Two pendulums at right angles to each other measure north-south and east-west changes.

deflection A of one pendulum and B of the other are combined vectorially into the resultant vector C, which represents the net horizontal component. Figure 62 shows a record of changes in magnitude and direction

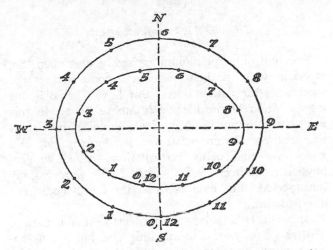

Fig. 62 A record of changes in magnitude and direction of the M_2 lunar semi-diurnal tide as time goes on.

of the M_2 lunar semi-diurnal tide as time goes on. The observation was made in Marburg, Germany. The outer ellipse is a plot of values calculated from theory for a rigid earth. Experimental values, shown by the inner ellipse, are everywhere smaller. This is to be expected if the earth yields. To give you an idea of the amount of deflection from the vertical involved in this record, the east-west change in angle is 0.0085 second of arc; the north-south change is 0.005 second!

The numbers appearing on the ellipses in Figure 62 represent lunar hours. Notice the phase difference of approximately one-half hour between experimental value and theoretical prediction. Both phase difference, and relative magnitude of the deflection compared to theory, can be quite variable with location. Also, the axes of the ellipses do not always coincide as well as they do here. In every case, however, the actual deflection is less than that predicted by theory.

Troubles due to indirect effects

The horizontal pendulum is highly developed. So, especially with the help of modern computers, is the analysis of the data it gives. But how reliable is our interpretation of the data? We are, as always in this field, trying to measure tiny effects. Small perturbations may entirely obscure what we are looking for. We know now that many perturbations—called by geophysicists "indirect effects"—exist. Some were entirely unsuspected until data revealed their presence. Let's discuss them.

One effect: a solar diurnal east-west fluctuation. This can hardly arise in anything else but a differential heating—and hence expansion-contraction—of the earth by the sun.

Another phenomenon noticed particularly at stations not in the centers of large continents: fluctuations which seem related to the ocean tides. How do we presume this relation? Because in general the tides of the sea differ considerably in phase from the tide-generating forces. The fluctuations exhibit this phase difference.

But how could ocean tides affect a horizontal pendulum firmly fixed to bedrock, perhaps hundreds of miles from the sea? There are two answers. First, ocean tides involve motions of vast quantities of water. The horizontal pendulum yields to the correspondingly varying attractions of these water masses. Second, we must think of the sheer weight of the water masses. When it's high tide along a coast, the sea bottom must support millions of extra tons of weight per square mile. Inevitably, the land sinks somewhat. And since the land is part of one coherent mass, the effect is an actual tilt of the crust for long distances inland. As the tide recedes, the crust tilts in the opposite direction. The horizontal pendulum, fixed to the crust, therefore records spurious tides, effects which obscure the actual earth tide we wish to study. In some regions spurious effects due to the sea can be truly enormous. Off the coast of Japan fluctuations 50 times greater than any which can be attributed to earth tides have been observed. In Bergen, Norway, on the other hand, the spurious and the true effects are of the same order of magnitude. It all depends, apparently, on local land structure. Much of Japan is situated along geologic faults. Here tilting of the crust in response to pressure can be very large—and also unpredictable. There are places where the tilt of the crust caused by the weight of water is in the wrong direction!

Evidently, faults act like the edges of elastic planes, planes which can flex separately. The same result on a larger scale, and not involving the ocean, can occur with the huge "tectonic blocks" which together form continents. If these blocks have different rigidities in various directions they can react differently to the tidal forces. If so, different stations in the same country may disagree seriously in their observations.

Also, don't forget the atmosphere! Its changing weight can have a large effect. Deviations of some 0.04 second from the vertical have been observed with the passage of a meteorological discontinuity—a warm air mass displaced by the arrival of a cold front. Compare this value with the maximum deviations which can be expected from the true tidal effect—deviations which, as stated a few pages earlier, are of the order of 0.01 second.

How to measure tilt

So much for a depressing enumeration of indirect effects. Not mentioned are several other effects fortunately smaller in magnitude. Now let's look briefly at modern techniques for measuring very slight deviations from the vertical.

The horizontal pendulum is constructed, typically, entirely of quartz. No mounting of man-made material—masonry, for example—is used, for such a material is never dimensionally stable enough. Rather, the instrument is set directly on geologically old bedrock, preferably deep in a mine shaft where temperature fluctuations are at a minimum. The table for the pendulum is fashioned without the use of explosives which might split the rock. Experience has shown that such an installation eliminates almost entirely the problem of drift in the reading of the instrument.

The problem of calibration is an important one, as it is for any measuring device. Calibration of an instrument as sensitive as a horizontal pendulum is formidable. The process typically consists of placing an expandable socket under one foot of the instrument. Motion of the socket gives an artificial tilt; the response of the pendulum to this tilt is observed. Meanwhile, the expansion of the socket is measured with an optical interferometer. This device records the displacement in terms of units which are wavelengths of light—perhaps of the red line of cadmium. The result: an extremely accurate measure of the amount of artificial tilt. Calibration to an accuracy greater than one-half of 1 percent is possible.

Sensitivities achieved with recently developed pendulums are sensational. For one instrument, motion of a millimeter on the recording paper represents a tilt of 0.0008 second! This figure is about 2 percent of the amplitude of the earth tides.

What a horizontal pendulum records is, of course, changes in angle between the frame of the instrument and the pendulum itself. The frame is fixed solidly to the earth, so that we may think of the whole device (except the pendulum) as rocking with the crust. The position of the pendulum itself, however, is determined only by the direction of the effective force of gravity in that region. Thus changes in the instrument reading reflect both tilt (arising for whatever reason) and variations in gravitation due to the tidal forces.

The subtleties of interpretation are, your author hopes, becoming clear by now. Let's summarize. On a completely rigid earth the horizontal pendulum would record only the tidal forces, which can be predicted in advance by theory. Observation shows, however, deflections less than this. It would be nice to say that the difference is due entirely to deformation of the earth by the tidal forces. The amount of this deformation could be calculated from the observations; then we'd have a quantitative description of earth tides. These results, in turn, would tell us much about the internal properties of the earth, to the joy of the geophysicists.

Alas, how do we separate out the indirect effects, the worst of which are those that lead to tilting of the crust for other reasons than tidal deformations? People have made valiant efforts. They have searched the pendulum data for periodicities and phase lags which might relate to the ocean tides. They have tried to calculate the gravitational attraction of water masses associated with these tides. They have assumed reasonable values for the elasticity of the crust, so that they might predict the amount of tilt due to loading of the coastline by tidal water. Then they have tried to apply their results as corrections to the pendulum data.

The work still goes on, but the task is difficult. There is good reason to hope, however, that these corrections, now very crude, can be refined. Then the worst, at least, of the indirect effects can be eliminated.

Effects of vertical components of tidal force

We ought now to ask: to what extent can earth tides be studied with gravimeters? The vertical components of the tidal forces, we have seen, change the effective magnitude of gravity; the earth's surface moves up and down as a result.

Gravimeters now exist which can record changes of at least one part in a thousand million of the earth's gravitational field—i.e., 10^{-9} g. The maximum change in gravity due to the astronomical tide-generating forces is, as we saw earlier in the chapter, about 10^{-7} g. Gravimeter technology, then, has advanced to the point where these instruments are useful in the study of earth tides.

The principle is this: deformation of the earth—the tidal bulge, and the resulting tensions and compressions—means a displacement of mass. The vertical component of gravity is therefore affected. Affected to a very slight degree, to be sure, since the largest component of the land tide, the M_2, apparently represents a rise and fall of only one to two feet. If you calculate the change in gravity corresponding to this relatively tiny change in the configuration of the earth, you find nevertheless that it lies within the range of sensitivity of modern gravimeters.

As in the case of the horizontal pendulum, we want to know the difference between the actual reading of the instrument and what it would read were the earth rigid. The latter can be calculated; the former, neglecting indirect effects, is modified by the bulge.

Now the effect of a given distortion can be estimated theoretically. We would hope, then, to find the actual amount of bulge by comparing the results of such calculations with the gravitational readings we observe.

There is much activity in the field. Gravimeters are in operation at many stations. Every station is strategically located for study of at least one of the various partial tides.

Happily, gravimeter readings are less subject to some of the indirect effects than are those of a horizontal pendulum. Nevertheless, the situation is discouraging. At a given station, it is true, plausible results seem to be generated. Unfortunately, the answers tend to vary drastically from station to station. The best guess: we are seeing effects due to local structural variations in the earth's upper mantle, variations leading to perturbations which obscure what we are looking for.

Direct measurement of crustal distortion and compression

The perceptive reader will have noticed a serious omission in our discussions so far. He will raise the question: can't earth tides be studied through direct measurements of distortions in the crust? In particular, how about stretching due to tensile stress? Tension will arise from the horizontal components of the tidal forces. Such stretching over any reasonable instrumental distance would be almost inconceivably small. Still, is its observation beyond our reach?

Why not go into a deep mine, where temperature variations are essentially nil, and tightly stretch a long, horizontal wire between rigid posts in the rock walls? Hang a weight from the center of the wire. Small changes in the distance between the posts will cause a greatly magnified up-or-down motion of the weight. This motion, in turn, can be effectively increased on an enormous scale by a suitable optical system.

Such experiments have been tried—in the United States, Japan, the USSR, and elsewhere. To date, the best that can be said of these experiments is that they do indeed *detect* crustal strains, but they cannot *measure* them with sufficient accuracy to contribute to our understanding of earth tides. Work is continuing. Perhaps in a few years the extensometer (a general term for the kind of instrument we are discussing) will be developed to the necessary degree of sensitivity. A step in that direction is the use of a laser beam in an exceedingly precise interferometer measurement. Another approach is the use of sensitive strain gauges placed in rock joints situated in caves. The gauges record relative slippage of the joints.

Compression-dilation, a volumetric effect, is another phenomenon accompanying earth tidal stresses. Like stretching, it should be small. Thus it is surprising that certain large-scale effects apparently result from it.

One such effect is the variation of water level in wells. Near a coast with a significant tide, the phenomenon is perhaps not too unexpected. Ocean load on shore areas is large, and crustal regions inland are thereby compressed. The flow of springs can be affected—a fact cited, indeed, by Pliny. One artesian well in France changes its flow (at a rate corresponding to the lunar semi-diurnal periodicity) from 60 to 90 gallons per hour during spring tides. Phase is that of the ocean tide, not of the astronomical forces. Thus the phenomenon is not due to earth tides as such.

But variations in wells or in flow of springs have also been recorded and analyzed at places far from oceans. These variations do have the proper phase relation to the astronomical forces. We can't calculate the amplitude of these tidal effects; the amplitude would depend on several factors such as the porosity of the soil and the volume of the confined water. But there are checks we can make. The ratios of the amplitudes for the different partial tides must correspond to theory. Also—and this is interesting—the phases of the oscillations (the rise and fall of the water, the increase and decrease of spring flow)—must be exactly opposite to those of the tide-generating forces. This is easy to see: effects leading to compression of the crust will decrease its porosity and force water out of it, raising the level of wells in the area.

Do experimental data confirm our guess that the phenomena are due to true earth tides? Without question. Positive results were obtained at many points in the United States, Africa, and Europe. Two wells have been studied intensively. One is at latitude 7° south in the Congo, the other at latitude 51° north in Belgium. (These latitudes are interesting; you will recall that the vertical component of the diurnal tidal force is zero at the equator and maximum at 45°.) For each well, amplitude ratios agree nicely with theory, and the phase differences work out to values comfortably close to 180° (opposite phase).

More recently, earth tides were studied at the flooded Reichenberg Mine in the state of Hesse in Germany. Analysis of data revealed eight of the short-period partial tides. Amplitude ratios and phase agree with the theoretical predictions.

Summary

The reader may feel that the discussion in the latter half of this chapter has been a collection of bits and pieces. Where does it all point? It looks as though there are true earth tides. What do we know about them? What, if any, quantitative statements can we make? It's time to summarize.

The earth yields elastically to the pull of the tidal forces. Several experimental methods, though differing in their relative accuracy, give at least this coherent result. If we ask how much the earth yields, the crucial question for geophysicists, the answer is less clear. Estimates range within wide limits. Indirect effects are so large and so difficult to predict and allow for that they seriously mask the actual amount of distortion.

We can make one positive statement, however. It is certain that the phase lag between the tide-generating force and the corresponding distortion is essentially zero. So we come to the important conclusion that the earth behaves elastically within the limits of the small strains imposed by the tidal forces. There can be little or no plastic flow.

We reluctantly admit that the study of earth tides to date is incomplete, insofar as we might hope to deduce information about the structure of the earth. The various earth models proposed by geophysicists predict different amounts of yielding to the tidal forces. Until we know better what this yielding is, earth tides can only be of limited help in choosing among the models.

Chapter X

TIDES IN THE ATMOSPHERE

Should we expect large air motion?

Tides in the atmosphere. Why haven't we spoken of them before? We've discussed water tides—the ebb and flow along ocean shores, and effects in small bodies of water. And now we've thought about tides in such a seemingly unlikely object as the solid earth.

Why have we neglected a whole medium in which we might expect tidal effects to exist? This medium, the ocean of air in which we live, is a fluid. Fluids, as we have seen, respond willingly to the smallest horizontal forces; we explained tides in the sea in this way.

Now air, having gravitational mass, is obviously subject to the same tide-generating forces that water experiences. The tidal force on a cubic foot of air is, of course, only a very small fraction of that on a cubic foot of water. On the other hand, air (except that at very low altitudes) is free to flow without encountering obstructions. We can, indeed, go back to Laplace's original concept of an earth entirely covered with fluid.

Naïvely, one might expect strong winds to blow, winds set up entirely by astronomical tide-producing forces. These winds would change their direction and speed periodically, at the command of the sun and moon.

But this does not happen and it should not happen.

Suppose you, as an aerodynamicist, calculate the amount of tidal force on a certain volume of air. You then compare the result with the frictional forces arising from the eddying and general turbulence which accompany mass transport of this volume. You find that the tidal force is by comparison very slight. A movement of air will take place, but you will scarcely have to lean into the gale to keep your footing! The motion is real but extremely slow. Even if it's slow, however, couldn't we observe it? No. The other forces which make wind blow are overpoweringly stronger. The situation is not comparable with that of the ocean, where the forces causing tidal currents are of the same magnitude as the forces causing other mass motions of water.

How to search for atmospheric tides in barometric data

How about another approach? Let's not talk about air movements. They're hard to measure precisely anyhow. Let's turn to that instrument called the barometer, capable of responding with great delicacy to changes in atmospheric pressure. Certainly tidal effects in the atmosphere, if they exist, are reflected in changes in barometric reading. Perhaps atmospheric tidal waves are set up. So why not just look for rise and fall of the mercury column, at periodicities which we can predict very well since we know the behavior of the tidal forces?

Alas, again we are foiled—or so it seems at first sight. Because of the normal passage of high- and low-pressure areas, plus local disturbances due to all sorts of factors—for example, unequal heating over various regions of the earth's surface, and storms—the barometer is a very lively instrument indeed. Compared to the changes in pressure one might expect from tidal forces, its rise and fall are tremendous. Much of its behavior is apparently random and unpredictable; that is to say, the meteorologist is faced by more variables than he can handle. He can foretell the general rise and fall accompanying the march of high- and low-pressure areas—"the normal course of the weather." But superimposed on this slow variation are pressure changes irregular in time and in magnitude. If you look carefully at the graph drawn by a recording barometer you will see no periodic pattern in the "secondary variations" we are talking about. There is no obvious evidence of any tidal effect. But we suspect it's *there*. Can we uncover it?

The problem as just stated is a very general one, encountered throughout experimental science and technology. It is the problem of *separating signal from noise*. The random variations in the instrument readings are the noise; the signal is a periodic function buried in the noise. In our case, noise is the large and irregular fluctuation of the barometer, and the signal is the expected periodic pressure variation due to tidal forces.

The problem is attacked by the method of harmonic analysis, a most interesting and fruitful procedure. The graph drawn by the recording barometer is to the eye a random and irregular one, containing no recognizable periodicity. If a small periodic variation in pressure is present, however, it is inevitably influencing the shape of the curve. One way to discover the signal if it exists: use the fundamental principle of resonance.

Let's take as an example something you are already familiar with, the tuning circuit of a radio receiver. As you turn the knob of the tuning dial, you are changing the resonant frequency of a circuit (consisting of a coil and a capacitor). Into this circuit are fed the radio signals picked up by the antenna. The output of the circuit goes to succeeding stages of amplification and detection.

The antenna is picking up, simultaneously, electrical signals of a myriad of frequencies, generated by all the transmitters whose waves are arriving at that location. Now the tuning circuit has, for a particular dial setting, one natural frequency of electrical vibration. If a signal of that frequency is fed into it from the antenna, large oscillatory currents of that frequency will be set up. These currents will be amplified and detected by succeeding stages in the radio receiver. The result: you listen to that station alone—i.e., to the transmitter having that particular frequency.

In a properly designed tuning circuit, the resonance is quite sharp (see Figure 63, in which response of the

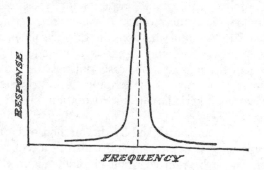

Fig. 63 Response of the tuning circuit of a radio receiver plotted against frequency.

circuit is plotted against frequency). The frequency to which the circuit is tuned at the moment is f_o; response to other frequencies is negligible. By turning the dial you "sweep" the resonant frequency f_o through various values, thereby tuning in different stations.

Can you see how to use this idea in our problem of picking a periodic signal out of noise? Let's somehow convert the jagged line drawn by the recording barometer into an electric current varying in exactly the same way. We could, for example, use a "photo-electric

scanner" whose tiny eye automatically follows a curve
drawn on paper. The mechanical motion of the eye as
it moves along the curve is translated into an electric
current. Figure 64 then can be considered either the

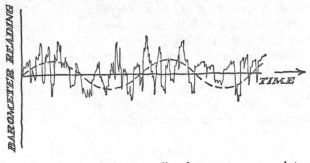

Fig. 64   Graph of the recording barometer or a plot of
the correspondingly varying current from a photo-electric
scanner.

original graph from the barometer or a plot of the
correspondingly varying current from the scanner.

Now send this current as input information into a
tuning circuit connected in turn to a suitable meter.
Slowly vary the resonant frequency of the circuit as the
electrical information is fed into it over and over again.
If a periodic variation of frequency f is present in the
input, there will be sudden indication on the meter
when the resonant frequency f_o becomes equal to f.
We have thus picked a meaningful signal out of apparently meaningless jumps of the barometer! The
signal can be very weak indeed compared with the
noise, and yet be detected and measured.

The process of course does not have to be one of
endless searching. We already know the periodicity of
the tidal forces. We can preset our electrical controls
for a particular period and see if it is there.

The preceding method lends itself to description;

you see the fundamental idea. In practice, you would program a high-speed computer to carry out the searching. The computer, however, would be doing in principle the operations we have just described. The searching for tidal effects has been done—long ago and laboriously, without modern computing aids. The results are extremely interesting. One has to examine a long series of barometric observations. The best data for the purpose are those taken at stations near the equator. They show variations in barometric pressure of periodicity corresponding to certain tidal rhythms. These periodicities amount to less than 1 percent of the average daily barometric variation!

Observed partial tides, and possible explanations

The largest by far of the observed tidal oscillations in pressure is the *solar* semi-diurnal cycle. On the equator, the pressure maximum occurs at 10:00 A.M. and 10:00 P.M. local solar time. Other periodicities found: a weak lunar semi-diurnal, a solar six-hour, and a solar variation occurring three times a day.

All this is at first glance very puzzling. Not so much the rhythms; they are presumably due to forced waves in the atmosphere. But we are used to thinking of the moon as much the more effective tide-producing agent. For atmospheric tides, however, its effect is discovered to be small in comparison with that of the sun. This immediately tells us something—something we might in fact have suspected from the beginning. The pressure variations are set up by atmospheric waves, and the largest waves are generated *not by gravitational tidal forces but by solar heating.*

If this is true, though, it raises a difficult question. Solar heating of the atmosphere should follow a solar *diurnal* cycle, not semi-diurnal. But the diurnal solar component is not observed. It is only fair to say that no one is sure of the answer yet. In a moment we shall make a plausible hypothesis, however.

First let's consider some general matters. We suspect that resonance between free and forced oscillation of atmospheric waves is causing the observed tidal periods. We call upon Laplace for the necessary theory, which attempts to describe waves in a fluid covering the entire earth. For oceanic tides we recall that depth of the sea was a crucial factor in the theory. The resonance of a tidal wave cannot be determined from its period alone.

For atmospheric waves, actual physical depth has little meaning. With increasing altitudes, the atmosphere becomes more and more rarified; there is no sharply defined "top of the atmosphere." In the equation for atmospheric waves, however, there appears a parameter called the *equivalent depth h.*

Now the theory says that free oscillation of the earth's atmosphere can take place only for one or more fixed values of h, called eigenvalues of h *and* denoted by $\hat{h}$. The numerical values of $\hat{h}$ depend on the kind of atmosphere under consideration.

What do we mean by "the kind of atmosphere"? There is only one atmosphere, isn't there? From the theorist's point of view the answer is that there are as many different atmospheres as you want to construct. In other words—and this is true throughout science—the theorist's first step is to create a simplified model of what he is trying to study. In the problem we are facing, the actual atmosphere is much too complicated. We cannot set up equations for it because we do not know enough about it. But we can make certain simplifying assumptions—i.e., construct a model atmosphere. If the model is simple enough, it will be amenable to mathematical analysis. Ordinarily, though, there are several models which at the beginning seem equally good. Each leads to theoretical prediction which can be compared with experiments. The test of the model is then the agreement of the predicted behavior with actual observation.

There's nothing new about these remarks. They are, in fact, a summary of one way in which science progresses. Throughout the book we have implicitly used the method just set forth.

To return to atmospheric waves: mathematical analysis says that the closer h is to $\hat{h}$, the higher the resonant magnification of the corresponding wave. This idea is not new to us. Now the main type of wave is a westward-migrating solar semi-diurnal oscillation. Why is this the main type rather than a solar diurnal? Laplace was in agreement with the idea that solar tidal waves are of thermal rather than gravitational origin, but he could not explain the absence of the diurnal period. Much later, Lord Kelvin suggested that the semi-diurnal wave may be a selected resonance of the atmosphere as a whole. By coincidence, one might say, h is very close to $\hat{h}$ for this particular wave type. He—and others—went on to develop what is now known as the resonance theory of atmospheric tides. It soon turned out that geostrophic effects were of great importance. In order to include them, severe simplifying assumptions had to be made about the nature and behavior of the atmosphere.

The absence of the solar diurnal oscillation was explained on the basis that presumably the free period of its waves corresponds to a value of h which is far from an eigenvalue $\hat{h}$. There are some theoretical implications that this is true.

So far we have said nothing of the origin of the solar tidal waves, except to suggest that they are thermally generated. First we must ask: how does the atmosphere absorb radiant energy from the sun? Most of the incident solar energy is contained in the visible range of wavelengths which can penetrate right through the atmosphere. The earth re-emits the energy it receives, but at much longer wavelengths—the infrared. Now it happens that water vapor, ozone, and carbon dioxide are strongly absorbent of infrared radiation, and so they trap the outgoing energy. This effect (sometimes called the *greenhouse effect*) is of the greatest importance. Without it, temperatures on the earth would be so low that no life could exist.

The atmosphere is, of course, far from static. Horizontal and vertical air currents exist at all times. Distribution of heat is constantly taking place by the interplay of convection, conduction, and radiation. Increase of temperature in one region is accompanied by expansion of the air. This expansion can in turn generate a pressure impulse and create a wave. Lamb,* one of the leading proponents of the resonance theory, wrote: "Without pressing too far conclusions based on the hypothesis of an atmosphere uniform over the earth, and approximately in convective equilibrium, we may, I think, at least assert the existence of a free oscillation of the earth's atmosphere, of semi-diurnal type, with a period not very different from but probably somewhat less than, 12 mean solar hours."

Chapman, in 1924, seemed to put the resonance theory on strong ground by accounting for the time at which the maxima and minima of the solar semi-diurnal oscillation occurred. He assumed that the thermal tidal forces are due to a temperature wave which spreads out from the earth's surface by turbulent motion ("turbulent mass exchange"). He was able to compute the corresponding pressure wave.

The author would like to pause at this point to ask

* *Proceedings of the Royal Society* A 84, 551 (1911).

the reader a question: Do you have any philosophical objection to the work we have been describing? The author does. It seems to him that we have been engaged in a scientifically very dangerous operation. We have *observed* an unexpected phenomenon—an atmospheric tide whose largest component is solar semidiurnal. We have *constructed a theoretical explanation* of this behavior simply to account for the particular phenomenon. The philosopher would say that the explanation is too *ad hoc*—too much restricted to doing this one specific thing.

Ad hoc assumptions are always suspect. Remember that other, weaker pressure waves have been observed, including a lunar semi-diurnal oscillation. More recent study has shown that the resonant magnification of the solar semi-diurnal wave is of the same order of magnitude as that of the other oscillations. It alone, then, is not favored by resonance. Furthermore, recent measurements at high altitudes do not confirm temperatures upon which the calculation of $\hat{h}$ was based. And the Kelvin theory is very vulnerable to this sort of thing; it implies sharp tuning of the condition of resonance. Sharp tuning in turn implies a relatively uniform air condition, and—in colloquial language—the atmosphere isn't that uniform. It's a horribly mixed-up affair. Land-water distribution on the earth's surface, for example, affects the location and magnitude of thermal forces. Water vapor density is greater above the sea. Also, seasonal variations should have a large effect. They are not observed.

Some considerations, then, suggest abandonment of the resonance theory. In that case, Chapman's explanation of heating by turbulent motion must go by the board, and another method of thermal excitation devised.

The most recent work on the subject attempts to

develop a theory of atmospheric tides *not* based on a strongly resonant solar semi-diurnal oscillation. Geophysicists are saying: It is not the semi-diurnal but the *diurnal* oscillation which is the extraordinary phenomenon. The semi-diurnal predominates because the diurnal is suppressed in spite of its stronger excitation. The new theory seems to have a larger validity; it can explain more observed facts.

It is obvious that much more theoretical work and observational data are required. The atmospheric models in use are not sophisticated enough, and a great deal of additional information on the behavior of waves other than the solar semi-diurnal is needed. Happily, high-speed electronic computation is going to help a lot with both of the enterprises.

At the moment, however, a completely satisfactory explanation of atmospheric tides does not exist.

Chapter XI

TIDES AND THE PLANETARY SYSTEM

The concept of time

How sophisticated are you about the concept of time? Time, you say, is an obvious matter. You are accustomed to its rate of passage; you accommodate your life accordingly.

It is true that the laws of relativity show time to be indeed only a local phenomenon. No such thing as absolute time exists; time's flow will be different for one observer and for another moving with respect to the first. But this difference becomes apparent only when the relative speeds of the observers are very high. Relativistic effects, says the physicist, need be taken into account only at velocities which are an appreciable fraction of the velocity of light.

This statement is true enough by ordinary standards. Even the speeds of celestial objects in our planetary system, enormous though these speeds may be compared with man's motions on earth, are miniscule in terms of the speed of light. Only in very specialized situations does the astronomer see (and by amounts so small as almost to be at the limit of detectability) any time effects which can be linked to relativity.

Why, then, do we imply any problem about time, as we prepare to talk of tides and their place in the behavior of the planetary system? Because the problem does exist; it lies in the human mind. Teachers of geology and astronomy agree that their hardest task, at the start of their introductory courses, is to instill a feeling for long, very long, time spans. Changes very slight in terms of a human lifetime become enormous for the existence span of the earth or of the universe in general.

To take an example from geology: the drift of continents over the surface of the globe (and certain theories and observations support the idea) goes on, if it does at all, at a very slow rate—slow in human terms. The displacement could be at most an inch or two per year. Negligible, says the neophyte in these matters. But the earth is perhaps 4.5 thousand million years old. Even if drift existed only over the past thousand million years, it is easy to calculate that in this time a continent could have moved thousands of miles!

We're making these preliminary remarks about time because tidal forces and effects, as we have come to realize, are miniscule in comparison with the large-scale phenomena of the solar system. Over cosmic time spans, however, they can and do alter the whole relation of a planet to its satellites. They also alter the rotation of the planet itself. How the tides do this, and what happens as a result, are the substance of this chapter.

How the moon can slow the earth

First let's take a look at how tidal forces, due, say, to the moon, can affect the rotation of the earth. We've seen how friction causes the tidal bulges to lag behind the earth-moon line; only for equilibrium tides does high water come when the moon is directly overhead. Figure 65 shows the situation, with the bulges greatly exaggerated as usual. The rotation of the earth, as drawn, is counterclockwise. The gravitational forces

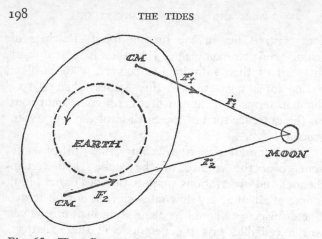

Fig. 65 The effect of tidal bulges, produced by the gravitational forces of the moon, on the earth's rotation.

produced by the moon on the two bulges are represented by F_1 and F_2. They are drawn as acting at the center of mass CM of each bulge. A crucial point: F_1 is slightly bigger than F_2 because the distance r_1 is less than r_2.

If F_1 is greater than F_2 the earth is not in rotational equilibrium. A torque or twisting action exists in a direction which, as you can see, tends to slow the earth's rotation. Thus by this argument the length of the day is increasing, and the earth is losing angular momentum.

Meantime, what is happening to the moon? By Newton's third law the moon feels forces equal and opposite to F_1 and F_2. They are depicted in Figure 66 by F_1' and F_2'. The solid line through the moon, perpendicular to the earth-moon line, represents the path of the moon in its orbit. The moon's motion along this path will be affected by any force which happens to have a component in that direction. Both F_1' and F_2' have such components. They are represented by the forces F_3 and F_4 respectively, which are obtained

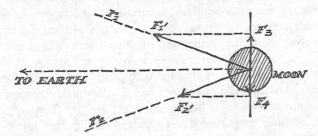

Fig. 66 The effect of the earth's rotation on the moon's revolution about the earth.

simply by starting at the tips of the arrows F_1' and F_2' and drawing lines which intersect the moon's path perpendicularly.

Now the moon is traveling upward in the diagram; the fact that F_3 is greater than F_4 means a net acceleration in the direction of the moon's motion. Thus, while the tidal forces are slowing down the rotation of the earth, the moon's *revolution* about the earth is becoming faster and faster.

This effect on the moon could have been predicted on more general grounds: the law of the conservation of angular momentum. Remember that we're considering only forces acting *within* the earth-moon system; such forces can have no effect on the total angular momentum of the system, which includes the rotation of the earth on its axis and the revolution of the moon in its orbit. If the rotation slows, the revolution must speed up—it's as simple as that.

Here, incidentally, is a nice example of how a fundamental conservation principle may be invoked to predict behavior of the system, without having to call upon the detailed laws which describe individual motions within the system. Physical science is, in fact, an edifice erected on a foundation of a few basic principles. These principles consist of conservation laws which in turn arise from certain invariances and symmetries characteristic of our universe. Our study of the tides involves only the principles of Newtonian mechanics. Here the use of invariances is pretty much restricted to conservation of momentum and energy. If our analyses involved the atom, we would quickly become aware of several other invariances, and of their overwhelming importance for understanding the microscopic world.

But to get back to our immediate problem. You may well ask: "Is it only the lagging oceanic bulge, then, which is slowing the earth's rotation?" No. Probably the ocean does produce by far the largest effect. But even if there were no ocean, a slight phase lag between tidal force and tidal bulge would exist. Why? Because we cannot conceive of the earth itself as *totally* elastic —as having, in other words, no internal friction loss whatsoever. These matters we considered in Chapter IX.

How about the sun, and the effect of solar tides? Tides, that is, raised on the earth by the sun's gravitational force. The answer: so far as the earth's rotation is concerned the consequence is the same—a slowing down. Moon and sun conspire to lengthen our day.

If part of the tides on the earth is raised by the sun, what happens to the moon as a result? Does its speed increase still more? No. In the long run, solar tides can have no effect on the moon. The reason is interesting. The periods of solar and lunar tides are different. In the course of a synodic month, then, solar tides are presented to the moon in all possible different aspects. During half the month they will accelerate the moon in its path, but during the other half they will decelerate it by an equal amount. The long-term average is zero. By the same sort of reasoning we can prove that lunar tides do not affect the sun.

But what of the effect of solar tides on the whole

earth-moon system? After all, according to our previous reasoning, some slowing torque should exist. It does, and what happens is that part of the earth's rotational angular momentum goes into an increase in the angular momentum of the whole earth-moon system in its orbital motion around the sun. The result is very small compared with other tidal effects in our planetary system. Calculations show that ten thousand million years would have to pass before any significant change occurs.

We've said nothing of the effects of tides raised *on the moon by the earth*. Aren't they important? No, and the reason is simple. The moon always presents the same face toward the earth (except for a tiny "physical libration," or rocking, whose effects are negligible). Thus the moon's tidal bulge caused by the earth is fixed with respect to the moon's surface, and is always toward the earth. No tidal torque can arise, thus no transfer of angular momentum.

We've applied the principle of momentum conservation to our arguments. Hadn't we better think now of an equally majestic invariance—the conservation of energy? Let's see what we can learn.

If the earth is slowing in its rotation, it is losing kinetic energy. If the moon is speeding up in its orbit, it is gaining kinetic energy. Are the two amounts equal and opposite, so that kinetic energy is conserved? No. In the first place, there is no such thing as a law for the conservation of kinetic energy—only for the conservation of the *total* energy of the system, whatever forms the energy may take. Secondly, we can predict on obvious grounds that the changes in kinetic energy will not cancel out. If they did cancel, we should be denying the very cause of tidal torque—frictional effects creating a lag in the bulge. And frictional effects directly imply a dissipation of energy in the form of heat.

What we have, in actuality, is a complicated interplay of various forms of energy. The earth's loss of rotational kinetic energy goes partly into heat, and partly into increased kinetic *and potential* energy associated with the moon's orbit.

Measuring the change in the day

Can we calculate the tidal torque? If so, knowing the moment of inertia of the earth, we can find the rate at which the day is lengthening. Also, we obtain information necessary to predict the future orbit of the moon.

Alas, no luck! We can't *calculate* tidal torque—at least, not directly from knowledge of the tidal bulge and its phase lag. Ocean tides are just too complicated, a fact that has been brought home to us again and again. And if body tides make a significant contribution we're even worse off, since they add a complicating factor whose effect is very difficult to estimate.

Which leaves us in the hands of the astronomers (and, it will turn out shortly, other and unexpected kinds of scientists), who come to our rescue—partly, that is. The astronomers point out that they might be able, by observation, to measure the rate of decrease of the earth's rotation—i.e., the lengthening of the day. Taking this value of deceleration, we could easily work backward and calculate the tidal torque. But as to the last—who cares? Tidal torque is simply the decelerating instrument. We are not interested in it but in its consequences—what happens to the earth-moon system as a result of tidal dissipation of energy.

"All right," we say to the astronomers. "Make your observations and tell us at what rate the earth is slowing down."

This request, it turns out, is not a simple one. Right now, in fact, we should be able to see some of its complications. In the first place, whatever the answer, it is going to be tiny, since the tidal forces are relatively so small. Furthermore, the process involves the measurement of *time*, and time, ordinarily, is determined by the rotation of the earth. An arrant contradiction!

Astronomers measure time by observing transits of stars across the meridian. The interval between two successive transits is the *sidereal day*; the earth has turned through exactly 360 degrees. The observatory has a standard clock. Its rate and its error are found by relating the instant of transit (taken over a series of days) with the corresponding reading of the clock.

If we are to use the rotation of the earth as a standard of time, we must obviously assume that the rotation is uniform. Astronomers have long been aware of one kind of nonuniformity: the *nutation*, or "nodding," of the earth's axis. As we saw in Chapter III, the direction of the axis is not fixed in space. It precesses. But (and this was not mentioned before), superimposed upon this motion are periodic variations in direction called nutation. The phenomenon affects slightly the measurement of sidereal time, but it can be fully corrected for. When this is done all sidereal days have the same length, assuming that the earth's rotation is constant.

But if the rotation is not uniform, how may we find it out? There are two ways. (1) Celestial mechanics is a very highly developed science. Positions of objects in the solar system can be predicted with great accuracy. The calculations assume of course a day of constant length. If the observed positions of the objects differ from those computed, the earth must have meantime changed its rate of rotation. What we are saying is, essentially, that the process compares the earth as a clock with, say, the moon, Mercury, and Venus as clocks. If deviations from prediction for all three of these objects correlate, then inevitably it is the earth clock, not the moon-Mercury-Venus clocks, which is at fault. (2) If we had man-made clocks precise enough, then variations in the length of the day are, in principle, directly observable. But we know in advance that the variations, whatever their nature, are extremely small.

For about thirty years astronomers have indeed had clocks of accuracy much greater than that of the long-standard pendulum type. A precision quartz-crystal oscillator is capable of an accuracy of 0.001 second per day. This clock makes use of the piezo-electric effect. A quartz crystal, properly cut, is put between two metal plates. When a voltage is placed across the plates an electric field is created between them. The crystal, under the action of the field, undergoes a mechanical distortion. Suppose the field is not constant in time; instead, an alternating voltage is applied to the plates. If the variations in voltage occur at just the same rate as the crystal would vibrate mechanically if left to itself (period of free oscillation), then resonance occurs. The vibrations of the crystal are enormously amplified, and the situation reacts on the electrical oscillatory circuit and "locks it in" to that particular frequency. The corresponding alternating current is used to drive an electric clock. The vibration of the crystal is somewhat temperature-dependent, but this difficulty is met by keeping it in a constant-temperature enclosure. The chief trouble is a slow drift in frequency due to aging effects. For short lengths of time, however, this is not a problem.

A still more recent development is the so-called atomic clock. Here time intervals are measured in terms of characteristic vibrations of certain molecules or atoms. The frequency observed is extremely stable in spite of changes in the physical environment. The clock can be made constant, in fact, to within one part in ten thousand million. Here, then, is an instrument far exceeding in its time-keeping potentialities any other clock yet conceived.

The atomic clock can be used by itself, or—and this is often the case for reasons of convenience—it can be used to monitor the quartz clock and correct for its long-term drift.

We have discussed two different ways in which non-uniform rotation of the earth might be discovered. Have they been pursued? Yes, in recent years, and with results which by either method are unequivocal.

Unexpected changes in the earth's rotation

The rotation of the earth is not constant. Departures from uniformity fall into three different categories: (1) a slow increase in the length of the day; (2) periodic variations, some of which seem to follow seasonal patterns; (3) random variations.

There is general agreement that the first is due to tidal friction. We'll talk more of this in a moment. But first, it's interesting to speculate on the causes of the other two variations.

As to the seasonal patterns: the earth seems to revolve slower in the spring, faster in the fall. There is, in other words, an annual periodicity. The total amount of speeding up and slowing down, in terms of range of length of day, is about two milliseconds. (We'll make use of the millisecond, abbreviated ms, as a convenient unit for expressing time fluctuations.) This change has been shown to be due largely to winds and the momenta associated with them. You can probably think of other possible reasons. How about changes in the earth's moment of inertia I due to weight of snow? (Incidentally, I doesn't change when icebergs float southward. By Archimedes' principle the mass per unit area of the ocean stays the same.)

How about added mass associated with the growth of
vegetation? How about changing ocean currents?

If you have a favorite possibility, you'd better forget
it. All have been examined, and all except winds are
found to have a negligible effect. It's pretty hard to
change the earth's moment of inertia. Someone has
calculated that if all American autos were driven from
Alaska to Mexico, it would change I by only one part
in 10^{14}! Or if the whole Central Asian high plateau
including the Himalayas were reduced to sea level,
the change in the length of the day would be less
than one millisecond!

There are other periodic variations. One is semiannual. It is smaller than the annual change; calculations show that part of it, at least, is due to body tides.

One variation in particular is very puzzling—puzzling because the period is of the order of decades.
Meteorological effects could only explain shorter
changes; geologic effects require time spans much
longer. In this middle range one theory alone holds
promise. It is highly technical, and we cannot go into
its details here. Broadly speaking, it recognizes that the
earth's magnetic field is evidence for complex motions
in the core of the earth. If the lower mantle is electrically conducting, electromagnetic torque will arise
from the turbulence of the core, and the rotation of
the earth can be affected.

Irregular variations in the length of the day are a
challenge to geophysicists. No explanation is at hand,
except that electromagnetic coupling may be playing
a part here also. The precision of atomic clocks allows
us to see these changes and in fact to measure them
with considerable accuracy. The variations may be
abrupt or of the order of years. For example, in July
1959 the length of the day seemed to increase suddenly
by 0.85 ms; then it slowly decreased at the rate of
about four microseconds per day. Certain physicists

have claimed that abrupt changes of this sort can be linked to violent solar eruptions, which are characteristically accompanied by intense emission of particles. But how this phenomenon could affect the earth's rotation is unknown. Another example of change, on a longer time scale: from June 1955 to January 1958 there was an almost constant deceleration of the earth, or increase in the length of the day. Whatever mechanism was at work, it was about fifty times more effective in producing deceleration than tidal friction!

History of the day's length

Now we are ready to speak of the slow and steady increase in the length of the day (sometimes called by geophysicists the "secular deceleration") which is clearly due to tidal friction. Here, our atomic clocks don't help us much. They were invented too recently. The deceleration we're studying is so small that the increase in the length of the day, from one year to another, is too little to measure. Measure in practice, that is. In principle it could be detected. But remember that this change is buried in much larger irregular variations. Only by following the length of the day for long periods of time—preferably centuries—can we average out the other variations and find that variation due to the tides alone.

How, then, do we go about measuring the secular deceleration? We'll speak of ways to do it in a moment. But to anticipate a bit: the average deceleration seems to be around 10^{-22} revolutions per second per second. Even if you're not used to thinking in powers of 10, this is obviously an extremely small number! Do a little arithmetic, and you'll find that the day has lengthened by perhaps two seconds in the past one hundred thousand years, or two milliseconds per century.

"Great heavens above," you say. "Why are you wasting almost a whole chapter in this book—and my time—in discussing an effect so minute?" Well, don't forget the first paragraphs of this chapter. What is small, and what isn't, depends on how you look at it. The history of the earth goes back perhaps 4.5 thousand million years. In a thousand million years, according to the above calculation, the day would have increased by several hours. And an increase such as this has caused, and will cause, all sorts of major changes in the earth and the moon and their relationship.

But to get back to our microscopic deceleration. How are we to measure it? Observations over a long time interval seem to be the only answer. What shall we do—try to find data among the records of the primitive astronomers? It isn't there, at least not in the direct form of a measurement of the day. And anyway, in that span of time the day hasn't changed enough. Perhaps, though, we can be a bit more subtle. We know the laws of celestial mechanics, and can calculate backward to find the exact time of ancient eclipses.

Suppose the length of the day has increased by 2 ms per century. Then over the past twenty centuries how much shorter was the day, *on the average*, than the present day? Answer: 20 ms. Now calculate the *accumulated time difference*. This is 20 ms multiplied by the number of days in twenty centuries, or

$$\frac{20 \text{ ms}}{\text{day}} \times \frac{10^{-3} \text{ sec}}{\text{ms}} \times \frac{365 \text{ days}}{\text{year}} \times 20 \text{ centuries} \times \frac{100 \text{ years}}{\text{century}} = 14{,}600 \text{ seconds}$$

which is just over four hours. Now we're getting somewhere! Our microscopic change in the length of the day—2ms per century—has transformed itself into a respectable span of time. What to do? Become a combination astronomer and ancient historian. Search for records of eclipses. Did they occur where and when our calculations say they should, calculations assuming a constant rotation rate for the earth? If a difference of some hours has accumulated, then we ought to find not only a discrepancy in the time of day when the eclipse occurred; it should also have been observed at a place *some tens of degrees of longitude* away from our calculated position!

Unfortunately the ancient records are maddeningly incomplete. If the observer wrote of where he was when the eclipse happened, he often neglected to mention the time of day—or vice versa. Furthermore, some descriptions are vague and fanciful. One may ask, "Is he describing an eclipse, or a big meteor, or a super-nova, or some other celestial phenomenon?" All in all, the uncertainty in ancient observations is of the same order as the discrepancies we are trying to detect.

What of "modern" astronomical observations, which means essentially from the year 1680 to the present? It is hard, on this shorter time scale, to separate tidal and nontidal effects. Progress has been made, how-ever; values of tidal deceleration make reasonable agreement with those from ancient eclipse data, con-sidering the large probable errors involved. The present rate of deceleration, given earlier in this chapter, is fairly well established even if no use is made of eclipse records from antiquity.

Evidence from the corals

How nice it would be if we could extend our obser-vations backward in time, not by thousands of years, but by hundreds of thousands or millions! Thereby we rule out human observations. But this is a good thing; our evidence would be more objective.

Some recent and exciting discoveries do let us go far

back in time. Paleontology—the study of fossil organ-
isms—comes to our rescue, and through a most unusual device. Certain fossil corals reveal, under the
microscope, a complicated structure of bands or rings
on the lower part of the conical skeleton. These are
typically corals whose shells are of calcium carbonate.

The bands represent growth periodicities in the same
way as do the rings of a tree. They are more complicated, however, because rate of growth of the shell apparently depended upon more factors than the annual
change of seasons. Annual rings can be seen, to be
sure, but there are "subrings" which can be related to
the months, and still finer structures (about twenty
to thirty bands per millimeter) which are apparently
daily growth rings!

Given this interpretation of the ring structure, a
whole new field of information is spread before us.
Count the number of daily growth rings from one
annual ring to the next, and you have the number of
days in the year for the geologic era in question!
We're not limited to one type of fossil and therefore
to one span of time. There are three groups: one from
the Mesozoic and two from the Paleozoic. Of the last
two, one is Devonian (fourth period in the Paleozoic
—about 370 million years ago). Here the count of
daily growth rings numbers some four hundred.

"How nice," a doubter might say. "Almost too good
to be true. So the Devonian year had four hundred
days. Then a coral *now living* ought to show 365
daily growth rings."

A reasonable remark, and a reasonable request for a
control on the experiment. But are there living corals
of the type we're studying? Yes, and they show daily
growth rings of a number around 360. People, incidentally, are studying the mechanism of formation of these
rings. Apparently the rate of secretion of calcium carbonate varies between night and day.

The monthly periodicities are extremely important, too. We've seen that as the earth slows down the moon speeds up. Devonian corals show months—lunar months—which average 30.6 days. (As yet, no one knows why one aspect of the coral growth is keyed to the moon's cycle.)

Let's do a little figuring. How many lunar months in a Devonian year? Just about thirteen. Now if we apply some straightforward laws of celestial mechanics, we find that the moon has increased its angular momentum during this time by 1.6 percent. The earth has therefore lost in rotational angular momentum by the same percentage. In terms of rate of loss of angular momentum, this is 3.9×10^6 newton-meters. And happy to say, this is the figure the astronomers give us, based on their observations during the past few centuries! In other words, their calculation for the increasing length of the day agrees with the evidence from the corals.

We've still not exhausted the information flowing from the cornucopia of the corals. One of the big questions about the changing length of the day involves the earth's moment of inertia. Has it been constant? If not, all bets are off as to actual tidal dissipation in the past. The mere fact of an increase, say, in I would easily account for the slowing of rotation. But if I doesn't change, there is a fixed relation of the month to the day. The coral counts say that this relation has indeed remained the same, at least within reasonably small limits of error. Shortly we'll be discussing the evolution of the earth-moon system in the light of tidal dissipation of energy. Information from the corals says that we can relegate to limbo all evolutionary theories (and there are several) which assume a significantly changing size (and therefore changing I) of the earth.

How is tidal energy dissipated?

Now let's talk of the tides. Can tidal friction account for the secular increase in the length of the day? If it can, at what rate must energy be dissipated? Knowing the energy associated with the earth's rotation, and the energy transferred to the moon, we calculate this dissipation. It amounts to some 3×10^{12} joules per second. Where does it go? There are two possible "energy sinks": fluid friction in ocean tides, and friction resulting from earth tides.

Until recent years, it was the fashion to discount the effect of body tides. Distortion of the earth caused by them can hardly be more than one part in a million. We've seen in Chapter IX that with such a small strain it's hard to imagine much departure from elastic behavior—and it's only by inelastic response that friction occurs and energy is lost in the form of heat.

So people turned to the ocean. Here there are two possibilities. Frictional loss should obviously occur in shallow areas where tidal currents interact with the bottom. And there may also be loss in turbulent tidal currents within the body of the ocean itself.

At this point we call upon the hydrodynamicist, a man who operates in a most difficult and mathematically demanding field. "Can you give us," we say to him, "at least an order-of-magnitude calculation of energy loss due to ocean tides? And also—if possible—an estimate of the relative importance of internal loss versus loss in shallow regions?"

He will answer our questions only in part. So little is known of internal currents in the ocean—where they occur, their speeds, the masses of water involved—that no real calculations can be made. He will say, however, that at present no satisfactory theory exists which could predict internal turbulence big enough—big enough, that is, to make this effect account for a large fraction of the energy dissipation.

All right, what about dissipation in shallow areas? Here, he says, we can do better—though our results are still crude. Physical details of the coastlines of the world are enormously complicated, but they are known. Speeds of tidal currents in bays and estuaries, and depths of water, all constitute a mountain of data available to a hydrographer who wants to calculate tidal friction. Several extremely competent scientists have tackled the problem. As may be expected, their estimates for various regions differ widely. But one important fact emerges: their work shows that the total needed energy dissipation can be accounted for by shallow area friction alone—a statement which is true, however, only within limits of error which are very large. By "very large" we mean uncertainties so great that the ocean dissipation may be only half the suggested value.

And here the matter stands so far as the oceans are concerned. We are not *forced* to invoke other mechanisms of energy dissipation. We know in any case that if ocean dissipation does not get rid of all the energy, it gets rid of at least a large part of it. Critics of ocean tides as the sole agent point out how hard it is to conceive of so much energy finding its way—being "fed into"—the shallow areas of the globe. The ocean tide must be analogous to a set of progressive waves converging on regions of dissipation, and there being absorbed. Physically, the process is like waves striking a beach.

And yet there is unmistakable evidence that tidal energy dissipation is enormous. One can calculate, using astronomical data, that all the tidal energy of the ocean is absorbed *once every ten hours!* There is no doubt that the rate of frictional dissipation is imposing.

Has the energy dissipation rate of the oceans, what-ever it may now be, changed with the years—over geologic time spans, that is? Coastline topography is much more rugged than it used to be. If most dissipa-tion is due to interaction with an irregular shore, the present rate of energy loss may be larger. But there are factors operating in the other direction. In the past the oceans were shallower than now, and this would tend to increase the dissipation. Perhaps such speculation is not fruitful; evidence from the corals implies a rather constant rate of increase in the length of the day.

Geophysicists whose specialty is earth tides are now tending to give these tides a larger role in energy dis-sipation. A phase lag of only a few degrees in body tide would account for the whole lunar retarding torque. But recall our chapter on earth tides. We sim-ply don't know enough about them yet to calculate their effect in the frictional dissipation of energy. Some people believe that they may account for as much as one-third of the retarding action—but this is indeed only speculation.

It is interesting that man himself has some control, albeit very small, over the rotational speed of the earth. When the tidal power installation at La Rance went into operation, total ocean tidal friction, and thus the rate at which the day becomes longer, increased. That is to say, the installation made it harder for water to fill and empty the estuary. Frictional forces were introduced by the dam and the turbines. Unlike or-dinary tidal energy loss, part of the energy dissipated went into production of useful power.

The earth-moon system—its past and future

So much for the mechanism of tidal energy dissipa-tion. What are its consequences for the earth, the moon? Tugging gently and persistently over the ages, tidal forces have significantly changed the rotation of the earth, and the way in which the earth shares its angular momentum with the moon. Can we now search out the history of the earth-moon relationship? Can we predict the course of this relationship as future eons pass by?

Yes and no. Let's start with the "no." Newtonian mechanics is symmetrical with respect to time. By that we mean that if $-t$ is substituted for t in the appropriate equations, we calculate backward instead of forward in time, and find the history of the system whose dynamics we now know.

The process of backward calculation cannot, however, answer the crucial question, "How did the moon originate?" Theories have been presented in endless succession; none is satisfactory. Favored for a while was the "resonance theory," according to which the moon and earth once formed a single object. The mechanical argument goes as follows. If separation occurred, calculations say that the event must have happened three or four thousand million years ago. The figure is based on where the moon is at present. Before separation all the angular momentum now in the earth-moon system was resident in the conglomerate mass that constituted the earth alone. Its rotation period would have been some four hours, with solar tides raised at twice this rate. But if the earth were largely fluid, a free vibration period of about two hours was already possible. Resonance could occur; the amplitude built up, said the proponents of this theory, until wild oscillations shook the planet. Disruption occurred, and material from outer regions of the earth broke away. The material soon formed a spherical object—our moon. Why a sphere? Because any system tends toward a condition of minimum potential energy—a basic principle of physics. A lot of particles attracting one another will arrange themselves into a sphere, since this is the shape corresponding to least gravitational energy.

Support for this theory came from the fact that the moon's density is relatively small. The moon must therefore be made up chiefly or entirely of rocky material, not the more dense materials characteristic of the earth's interior. And the theory has already presupposed that the tidal disruption involved only the outer part of the earth.

Just as an aside: this "lightness" of the moon is currently a serious problem for astronomers. Not merely lightness in the sense of over-all density, but also from the point of view of mass distribution. The I which we calculate for the moon puts too much of the mass near the surface. It's as if the density increases as you go outward from the center—and this is completely at odds with structural considerations. Is the moon hollow?*

We've been using the past tense in speaking of the resonance theory, and with good reason. It's no longer a respectable explanation of the moon's origin. Too many sound criticisms exist. For example, recent calculations show that internal friction would have prevented large oscillations—and large, very large, oscillations are necessary for disruption.

Other theories of origin are based on the idea that the moon began as a separate body. Perhaps it is a fragment of stellar matter, left circulating around the sun after breakup of a companion star. Or perhaps the moon condensed from a diffuse rotating cloud of gas

* Data from the tracking of Lunar Orbiter spacecraft have recently been analyzed. The results indicate a moon of more or less uniform density, though the density may increase somewhat toward the center. The question as to why the density does not become rapidly greater with decreasing radius is still unanswered.

and dust. None of these theories can be substanti-
ated. In summary—we just don't know where the
moon came from.

At any rate, there is evidence that the moon was
molten at one stage. It has a permanent bulge on the
side toward the earth. The bulge is so large as to suggest that it solidified from a liquid under circumstances
when gravitational force due to the earth was much
greater than it is now. So probably the moon was a
good deal closer. Why is the bulge still there? The
material of the moon must have enough structural
strength to keep the bulge from collapsing.

Fortunately, we don't have to know the origin of
the moon to make predictions about the future of the
earth-moon system. The behavior will be governed by
the tides. Under their influence the rotation of the
earth is slowing. Rotational angular momentum is being transferred to the moon, which therefore moves in
an orbit of increasing radius. Greater radius means a
longer period of revolution—i.e., the lunar month is
getting longer as well as the day.

As this goes on, however, the moon will continue to
present the same face toward the earth. Why should
this be? Or—a better question—what is there in general about the earth-moon relationship that lets us see
only half of our celestial companion? Not until the
technology of lunar rockets and of television telem-
etry evolved could we know the secrets of the other
side.

As we said earlier, a physical system always tends to
seek a situation in which its potential energy is at a
minimum. Then it will be in a state of equilibrium. For
the moon, keeping one face toward the earth must
represent such a state. How was it reached? By tidal
dissipation *on the moon*. Both earth and moon were
almost surely fluid at one time. Hydrodynamicists have
evolved equations linking, for a fluid object, the rate of

tidal dissipation and the size and mass of the body. These equations state a remarkable fact—that dependence on size is so great that the moon would have changed its rate of rotation seventeen thousand times as fast as the earth. The moon, in other words, would have come to stop its rotation with respect to the earth long before the earth's rotation had been greatly affected.

It is true that the moon could not have remained fluid for long. As a relatively small object it cooled fast. Also, as a small object, its gravitational field was insufficient to retain any seas or atmosphere. Subsequent tidal dissipation in the moon could only come from body tides. But meanwhile the bulge toward the earth had formed. This bulge, for dynamical reasons, points slightly—very slightly—to one side of the earth-moon line. The gravitational field of the earth exerts, then, a tiny torque on the bulge. It is this torque that reduces the moon's rate of rotation and keeps it always with the same face to us.

What is to come of all this? We need only turn to celestial mechanics. The answer seems unequivocal. Inexorably the earth slows its rotation, inexorably the moon moves farther away. The month lengthens, but not as fast as the day. So there will come a time when the day and the month are the same—about fifty of our present days. Each object keeps the same face toward the other. They will be some forty percent farther apart than at present. Lunar tidal action on the earth will cease, except for a small effect; eccentricity of the moon's orbit will make lunar gravitational force on the earth vary. Thus the earth's bulge toward the moon will regularly pump up and down, with some small dissipation of energy.

So do matters end in this strange mutuality of experience? Do moon dwellers forever after contemplate a changeless earth, even as we have contemplated a changeless moon?

No. We've forgotten that solar tides on the earth are still at work. Still there is dissipation of energy, and still the earth's rotation slows. Behold, the day becomes longer than the month! Our descendants— if any remain after these eons—will see the moon move backward in the heavens. Backward, that is, with respect to what we now call its forward motion.

Lunar tides will be reborn. High tides will still occur after the moon has passed the zenith or the nadir. *But*—note well—they will be in symmetrically opposite positions with respect to the earth-moon line, compared to now. (Just rotate the bulges in Figure 65 through 90 degrees.) And so, a torque in the other direction. Now the feckless earth says to its satellite, "come back" —but with evil intent, as we shall see. Why does the moon return? Because this new torque slows its motion—and energy conservation then demands a lesser orbit. Both day and month shorten, but the day always remains longer than the month. Implacably, over long geologic ages, the partners approach one another. Tides raised in the moon by the earth grow to frightening size; the moon's surface heaves into mighty tidal mountains. Suddenly, no longer can the moon endure such forces. Broken into a thousand pieces, it probably forms a structure around the earth which might be compared to Saturn's rings.

So say the equations. But the time scale necessary for the process is incredibly long—much more than a few thousand millions of years. Other unforeseen celestial events may intervene; perhaps the moon will escape this particular fate.

What of tidal effects in other parts of the planetary system? We can make certain general statements. Obviously, solar tides affect all planetary rotations— usually to a very small degree, however. If the planet has one or more satellites other tidal forces appear. All satellites whose period is known keep the same faces toward their primaries. But the earth is unique in possessing a moon large enough to raise significant tides. Mars has two satellites, Phobos and Deimos, both of very small mass. Their influence on the rotation of Mars is negligible, but for the same reason Mars' effect on them is enormous. Recent studies indicate that Phobos is approaching Mars rapidly and will collide in a few million years. This is a length of time extremely short by astronomical standards—almost overnight, so to speak.

EPILOGUE

And so we come to the end of our voyage of discovery. We left port armed with the most meager of navigational tools: knowledge of gravitational force, earth to moon and earth to sun. This knowledge we chose as our guiding star; by it we set a course to seek out tidal behavior. On the journey we met a multitude of phenomena, some obviously to be expected, some strange and even inexplicable; some trivial, some of overreaching majesty. Looking back, we count with surprise how many different areas of physical science we entered, including study of the planetary system itself and its unknown infinities of time.

Why not revisit some of these areas? I have listed, on the next page, readings to lead you farther in understanding. Better yet, make a journey in person. Go to the shore of the sea; look now with new insight at what is happening. I have watched the ocean for many years, but I still see every day and on every hand new and wonderful things. *Bon voyage!*

SUGGESTIONS FOR
ADDITIONAL READING

BASCOM, WILLARD, *Waves and Beaches*. Garden City, New York: Doubleday & Company, Anchor Books, 1964, 257 pages.

Find out more about waves in this fascinating volume, also in the Science Study Series.

DARWIN, GEORGE H., *The Tides*. San Francisco: W. H. Freeman and Company, 1962, 369 pages.

An extremely readable and useful book despite its age, containing the substance of a course of lectures that Darwin delivered at the Lowell Institute, Boston, in 1897.

DEFANT, ALBERT, *Physical Oceanography*, Volume II. New York: Pergamon Press, 1961, 570 pages.

For an understanding of the more technical aspects of the tides, this is an excellent book by one of the leading authorities on the subject.

GAMOW, GEORGE, *Gravity*. Garden City, New York: Doubleday & Company, Anchor Books, 1962, 146 pages.

A nontechnical, highly readable, and unique presentation by the famous author and physicist.

KING, CUCHLAINE A., *An Introduction to Oceanography*. New York: McGraw-Hill Book Company, 1963, 337 pages.

A good way to extend your knowledge to ocean processes other than the tides.

MACMILLAN, D. H., *Tides*. New York: American Elsevier Publishing Company, 1966, 240 pages.

Emphasizes the practical aspects of ocean tidal theory and provides much numerical data.

INDEX